REVISE BTEC NATIONAL
Creative Digital Media Production

REVISION WORKBOOK

Series Consultant: Harry Smith

Authors: Julia Sandford-Cooke, Philip Holmes,
Lesley Davis and Sarah Holmes

A note from the publisher

While the publishers have made every attempt to ensure that advice on the qualification
and its assessment is accurate, the official specification and associated assessment
guidance materials are the only authoritative source of information
and should always be referred to for definitive guidance.

This qualification is reviewed on a regular basis and may be updated in the future.
Any such updates that affect the content of this Revision Workbook will be outlined at
www.pearsonfe.co.uk/BTECchanges.

**For the full range of Pearson revision titles across KS2,
KS3, GCSE, Functional Skills, AS/A Level and BTEC visit:**
www.pearsonschools.co.uk/revise

Published by Pearson Education Limited, 80 Strand, London, WC2R 0RL.

www.pearsonschoolsandfecolleges.co.uk

Copies of official specifications for all Pearson qualifications may be found on the website:
qualifications.pearson.com

Text © Pearson Education Limited 2017
Typeset and illustrated by Kamae Design, Oxford
Produced by Out of House Publishing
Cover illustration by Miriam Sturdee

The rights of Julia Sandford-Cooke, Philip Holmes, Lesley Davis and Sarah Holmes to be identified
as authors of this work have been asserted by them in accordance with the Copyright, Designs and
Patents Act 1988.

First published 2017

20 19 18 17
10 9 8 7 6 5 4 3 2 1

British Library Cataloguing in Publication Data
A catalogue record for this book is available from the British Library

ISBN 978 1 292 15023 9

Printed in Slovakia by Neografia

Acknowledgements
The publisher would like to thank the following for their kind permission to reproduce their
photographs:

(Key: b-bottom; c-centre; l-left; r-right; t-top)

123RF.com: khatawut Chaemchamras 37l; **Cobra Beer / Molsonbeer Corporation:** 5;
Fotolia.com: pictoores 37c, 37r; **Getty Images:** Alan Spencer 26; **Greene King Press Office:** 7;
Hattrickproductions: Outnumbered 12, 13, 14; **Image courtesy of The Advertising Archives:**
Fabric & Home Care / Procter & Gamble 2; **Universal Clips:** 9, 10

All other images © Pearson Education

Note from the publisher

Pearson has robust editorial processes, including answer and fact checks, to ensure the accuracy
of the content in this publication, and every effort is made to ensure this publication is free of
errors. We are, however, only human, and occasionally errors do occur. Pearson is not liable for any
misunderstandings that arise as a result of errors in this publication, but it is our priority to ensure
that the content is accurate. If you spot an error, please do contact us at
resourcescorrections@pearson.com so we can make sure it is corrected.

Websites

Pearson Education Limited is not responsible for the content of any external internet sites. It is
essential for tutors to preview each website before using it in class so as to ensure that the URL
is still accurate, relevant and appropriate. We suggest that tutors bookmark useful websites and
consider enabling students to access them through the school/college intranet.

Introduction

This Workbook has been designed to support you in preparing for the externally assessed units of your course. Remember that you won't necessarily be studying all the units included here – it will depend on the qualification you are taking.

BTEC National Qualification	Externally assessed units
Extended Certificate (DFVP, DCP and DGP)	3 Digital Media Skills
For both: Extended Certificate Foundation Diploma	1 Media Representations 8 Responding to a Commission
Diploma	3 Digital Media Skills 8 Responding to a Commission
Extended Diploma	1 Media Representations 3 Digital Media Skills 5 Specialist Subject Investigation 8 Responding to a Commission

Your Workbook

Each unit in this Workbook contains either one or two sets of revision questions or revision tasks, similar to those you will be set for your actual assessment. Working through these will help you to become familiar with the way in which you will be assessed and to develop the skills you require.

This Workbook will often include one or more useful features that explain or break down longer questions or tasks. Remember that these features won't appear in your actual assessment!

> Grey boxes like this contain **hints and tips** about how to complete a task, interpret a brief, understand a concept or structure your responses.

 This icon will appear next to a **partial sample answer** to a question or task outcome. You should read the partial answer carefully, then complete it in your own words.

> This is a revision activity. It won't be one of the outcomes you need to produce in your actual assessment, but it will help you understand the processes you will need to go through.

> 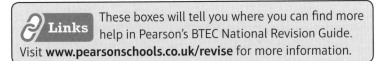 These boxes will tell you where you can find more help in Pearson's BTEC National Revision Guide. Visit **www.pearsonschools.co.uk/revise** for more information.

There is often space on the pages for you to write in. However, if you are carrying out research and making ongoing notes, you may want to use separate paper. Similarly, some units will be assessed through submission of digital files, or on screen, rather than on paper. Make sure you read the guidance for each unit that is given to you by Pearson and your tutor.

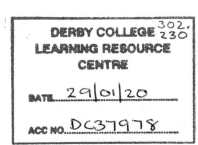

Contents

Unit 1: Media Representations

Unit 3: Digital Media Skills

Unit 5: Specialist Subject Investigation

Unit 8: Responding to a Commission

A small bit of small print

Pearson publishes Sample Assessment Material and the Specification on its website. This is the official content and this book should be used in conjunction with it. The questions in this book have been written to help you practise the knowledge and skills you will require for your assessment. Remember: the real assessment may not look like this.

Unit 1: Media Representations

Your exam

Unit 1 will be assessed through an exam, which will be set by Pearson. You will need to use your understanding of how different media representations are constructed by media producers to create meaning, messages and values. You then respond to questions that require short and long answers.

Your Revision Workbook

This Workbook is designed to **revise skills** that might be needed in your exam. The selected content, outcomes, questions and answers are provided to help you to revise content and ways of applying your skills. Ask your tutor or check the **Pearson website** for the most up-to-date **Sample Assessment Material** to get an indication of the structure of your exam and what this requires of you. The details of the actual exam may change so always make sure you are up to date.

To support your revision, this Workbook contains two sets of revision questions to help you revise the skills that might be needed in your exam. The first revision test helps consolidate your knowledge and skills in analysing a range of features in different media types. The second revision test gives you questions on a single clip to allow you to practise writing the types of answers required for your assessment.

Your exam questions

There is guidance in this Workbook for the skills involved in answering the following types of questions.
- Give
- Identify
- Explain
- Compare
- Analyse
- Assess
- Evaluate
- To what extent

Links To help you revise skills that might be needed in your Unit 1 exam, this Workbook contains two sets of revision questions starting on pages 2 and 12. The first is guided and models good techniques, to help you develop your skills. The second gives you the opportunity to apply the skills you have developed. See the Introduction on page iii for more information on features included to help you revise.

Revision test 1

To support your revision, this Workbook contains revision tests to help you revise the skills that might be needed in your exam. The details of the actual exam may change so always make sure you are up to date. Ask your tutor or check the Pearson website for the most up-to-date Sample Assessment Material to get an idea of the structure of your exam and what this requires of you.

Answer ALL questions. Write your answers in the spaces provided.

> **Guided**

1 Look at the following print advertisement for laundry conditioner.

(a) Explain **one** example of how colour is used to create meaning in this advertisement. **2 marks**

The mother and child are wrapped in a

red and gold blanket. These are both

....

colours that create a sense of ....

....

....

This implies that using ....

....

....

will also create these feelings.

> **Explain** questions require you to show your **knowledge** and **understanding** of the topic by giving reasons and examples to support your answer. The question will tell you how many examples of the feature you must explain.

> **Links** See pages 18 and 20 of the Revision Guide for information about how colour creates meaning in media representations.

(b) Explain **one** example of how typeface is used to create meaning in this advertisement. **2 marks**

The text in the centre of the advertisement uses a .... font.

The irregular letters give the impression that the text has been written by ....

....

The contrast with .... in other parts of the

advertisement attracts our interest and encourages ....

> **Links** See page 29 of the Revision Guide for information about how typefaces and fonts create meaning in page layouts.

(c) Identify **four** conventions of visual advertising that are present in this example.

1 Brand logo and ....

....

2 ....

....

3 ....

....

4 Reliance on symbols and ....

> Remember that all **advertisements are intended to persuade** the target audience to do something, in this case to buy a particular product. The conventions of visual advertising are included for this purpose.

> **Links** See page 3 of the Revision Guide for information about typical conventions of visual advertisements.

(d) Analyse **how** page layout is used to make an emotional impact on the viewer of this advertisement.

Page layout should follow certain conventions so

that readers are able to identify the most

.... elements of the

page, which order to look at them and how

to take action. The design must follow a

> **Analyse** questions require you to break something into parts by considering media representations methodically and in detail. This will help you to interpret the interrelationships between the media text, its context, audience and potential meaning.

.... visual hierarchy so that the reader can

....

In this advertisement, the eye is drawn to the large photo, which dominates the page. This image

shows ....

.... , and is larger than

the photo of the product itself in the bottom right-hand corner. This emphasises ....

....

....

The rule of thirds is demonstrated by ....

....

The child-like handwriting font has the affect of ....

....

....

....

> **Links** See page 29 of the Revision Guide for information about how page layout and composition create meaning.

(e) Evaluate the ways in which this advertisement is targeting mothers as the audience for the product.

6 marks

The advertisement features a large photo of

.... ,

which we assume represents ....

....

They are ....

....

....

This implies that .... ,

.... The target audience for this advert is

.... This has been

chosen because .... ,

....

.... The main text reads: 'It's more than a blanket; it's my secret

power to make her smile'. This anchorage reinforces the message that ....

.... The absence of male figures from the scene suggests that ....

....

Similarly, the selective representation of a mother and child sharing an intimate moment is likely to

appeal most to ....

> **Evaluate** questions require you to demonstrate your ability to fulfil the learning outcome: 'Apply knowledge and understanding of media concepts, semiotics, theories and formal techniques to constructed representations'. The answer provided here uses key terms, such as 'anchorage', 'absence' and 'selective representation', to show the ability to apply knowledge to the question.

Total for Question 1 = 20 marks

Guided **2** Watch the advertisement for Cobra beer, available by scanning the QR code or entering the URL in your browser.

Watch the clip here

http://activetea.ch/2mmjDDc

(a) Explain one example of how intertextuality is used in this advertisement. **2 marks**

One example of intertextuality is the references to

James Bond films, for example ....

....

....

....

> Intertextuality depends on the audience actively making connections to other media. Some media products refer directly to each other, in this case with the strong references to James Bond films. The audience creates meaning by being aware of these references (or not).

 Links See page 12 of the Revision Guide for more information about active viewing and intertextuality.

(b) Identify how costume and figure expression combine to represent 'the boss'. **4 marks**

'The boss' is always seen wearing .... clothes – the first shot of him focuses

on his designer leather .... ; he pays enough attention to detail to include a

handkerchief in his breast pocket; and later he wears .... This positions him

as rich and careful about the impression his appearance has on others. He makes eye contact with

.... , suggesting he is ....

Links Costume and figure expression are part of the *mise-en-scène*. See page 27 of the Revision Guide for more about this aspect of representation.

(c) Explain how 'the boss' is portrayed as conforming to a representation of stereotypical masculinity. **6 marks**

Mulvey's theory of ....

....

states that men are often portrayed as ....

.... , all of which 'the boss' is shown to be. He is an 'alpha male', so both men and

women do as he asks, and he has control over the manufacturing of both a traditionally masculine

product (.............................) and a sexualised feminine product (.............................).

He is, to some extent, objectified as the man living the ultimate male dream.

> Stereotypes are a way of quickly conveying information about a group or character so that the audience makes assumptions about the person being represented. This question asks you to explain how a stereotype is constructed in this advertisement. It is useful to refer to the main theorists and key terms (such as 'objectified') in a question like this.

Links Revise Richard Dyer's theory of stereotyping on page 8 of the Revision Guide, and Laura Mulvey's theory of audience positioning on page 9.

(d) 'This advertisement encourages oppositional readings.' To what extent do you agree with this statement?

8 marks

When a question asks **to what extent**, you need to give clear details and evidence to support your opinion.

In an oppositional reading, the decoder may

....

....

....

Start by demonstrating that you understand the term 'oppositional reading'. Then apply it to the media text being analysed.

In this advertisement, the preferred meaning at first seems to be

that the audience should aspire to ....

....

An oppositional reading may be that the viewer doesn't agree

that ....

....

....

....

....

Give some examples of oppositional readings in the context of the media text.

Although the advertisement can be taken at face value, as

portraying .... , it is also open to

oppositional readings. It can be viewed as a pastiche of portrayals

of .... men, such as James Bond, and is

clearly intended to be humorous. When 'the boss' winks at the end, we are led to question our

previous assumptions and consider whether ....

....

....

....

Remember to state your opinion about whether you agree with the statement.

....

....

....

Add your own thoughts about whether the advertisement encourages oppositional readings.

Links Revise audience decoding and reading on page 11 of the Revision Guide.

Total for Question 2 = 20 marks

3 Watch the following advertisement for Greene King IPA, available by scanning the QR code or entering the URL in your browser.

Watch the clip here

http://activetea. ch/2mJHJdW

(a) Identify the lighting technique used in the first shot. 　**1 mark**

> **Identify** questions require you to use your knowledge to select the relevant information from the stimulus material.

....

> **Guided**

(b) Explain why this lighting technique has been used. 　**3 marks**

.... lighting gives a

three-dimensional appearance and adds drama. This striking opening

shot engages the viewer's attention at once. The black and white

.... of the man's face highlights his

....

on what is revealed in the next shot to be a barrel.

> There may not be a single 'right' answer to many questions, you just need to make sure that your interpretation is appropriate to the context.

> 🔗 **Links** 　See page 19 of the Revision Guide for more information about how different lighting techniques create meaning.

(c) Identify **one** example of non-diegetic sound in the advertisement. 　**1 mark**

....

....

> Examples of non-diegetic sound are musical soundtracks, voiceovers and dramatic sound effects.

> **Guided**

(d) Explain how the representation of the pub is established through sound and lighting. 　**5 marks**

The pub is represented as welcoming and relaxed, where people go to have a good time. This is

established through both .... and ....

....

The music is initially muffled while the man is in the cellar but, as he ....

...., it becomes clear, drawing the viewer

into the pub's atmosphere. The lighting in the pub is ...., with a

yellow tinge, reinforcing the relaxed, warm feel of the bar. Most of the customers are

.... and in semi-shadow, helping to create a sense of intimacy.

> You could make several points about the sound and lighting but remember to include the correct terminology (e.g. 'diegetic', 'non-diegetic', 'backlit') to show you know and understand them.

> **Links** Revise creating representations via sound on pages 23 and 24 of the Revision Guide, and representations via lighting on page 19.

> **Guided**

(e) Compare the representation of the man in this advertisement with that of 'the boss' in the Cobra advertisement (Question 2).

`10 marks`

Neither man speaks; however, we get a clear idea of their characters. 'The boss' is ....

....

....

....

....

> Although neither man has any dialogue, you can gain a fairly clear impression of what they are like from the *mise-en-scène* – by looking at their costume, the props they use, how they interact with others and their figure expression. Consider what assumptions you are expected to make about their social class and attitude.

We assume that the man in the Greene King ad is also a boss, perhaps the landlord of the pub, but, unlike 'the boss' in the Cobra ad, his position is implied by ....

....

Unlike the Cobra boss, whose costume of expensive suits implies he is ....

.... the Greene King boss is dressed similarly to those around him, suggesting ....

Both men seem to take special care of the products they are in charge of – the Cobra boss directs the detailed production of .... and

...., while the Greene King boss personally prepares

.... he is about to serve.

> You could go on to talk about the possible meanings of the men being represented as loners, their attitude towards the activities around them, and their comparative levels of contentment. It might be argued that, although at first they seem very different, there are several similarities between the two men. Continue the answer with three or four more relevant points.

....

....

....

....

....

....

....

....

....

Total for Question 3 = 20 marks

4 Watch the following film clip, a trailer for the film *Miss Pettigrew Lives for a Day* (2008), available by scanning the QR code or entering the URL in your browser.

Watch the clip here

http://activetea. ch/2mmC8HO

(a) Explain **one** example of how colour is used to create meaning in the shots set in the apartment.

2 marks

The dominant colour in the apartment scenes is .... The walls, decorations and other props are .... , as are Delysia's dressing gown and hair. This colour implies ....

....

In contrast Miss Pettigrew's clothing and ....

This suggests ....

- You can write about any relevant aspect of the *mise-en-scène*, for example, location, props or costume. Identify the dominant colour and consider why this colour was chosen. What is its significance in relation to other colours, for example, the brown of Miss Pettigrew's coat?
- Remember to note the number of marks that will be given for each question. This will give you a clue as to how long to spend on each one.

Links You can revise the meanings created by colour choices on pages 18 and 20 of the Revision Guide.

(b) Explain how props and figure expression have been combined to represent Miss Pettigrew in the first minute of the trailer.

3 marks

The first shots of Miss Pettigrew suggest she is .... Her figure expression is downcast – she looks .... and walks with her head .... Her costume is ....

- This question offers a lot of scope for covering different aspects of the *mise-en-scène*, and there is no one right answer; however you should focus on props (which can include costume) and figure expression.
- You might find it useful to watch the opening minute with the sound turned off, so that you are not distracted by the voiceover or other aspects of the soundtrack. You can make a lot of assumptions about Miss Pettigrew through visual clues alone.

and she appears to be wearing no make-up. This implies ....

.... This is reinforced by the contrast with

.... Miss Pettigrew displays a shocked, disapproving expression several

times while in Delysia's apartment, suggesting she is ....

.... However, she can also be rebellious, for example by

....

🔗 **Links** See page 27 of the Revision Guide for more information about the meanings and representations created by the *mise-en-scène*.

(c) Identify the camera position shown in this still.

1 mark

....

🔗 **Links** You should be able to identify a number of different camera positions and shots, which you can revise on page 16 of the Revision Guide.

Guided

(d) Explain why this shot has been used.

2 marks

It is used to show ....

....

and draws the audience into ....

....

It can also provide extra information about what

is happening by ....

The angle and height of the camera can communicate a lot of information to the audience about characters, setting and narrative. Particular shots will have been chosen for a reason so consider this in both general terms – what a shot like this communicates – and how it specifically applies to the example.

....

(e) Identify the genre of *Miss Pettigrew Lives for a Day*.

1 mark

....

There may be more than one right answer but you must decide on one and be able to give convincing reasons for your choice in (f) below.

(f) Explain **three** conventions shown in the trailer that fulfil this genre.

3 marks

1. ....

2. ....

3. ....

Choose the three most obvious conventions you can identify. Use specific examples from the trailer to back up your answers.

🔗 **Links** You can revise genre expectations and subversion on page 14 of the Revision Guide.

(g) 'This trailer reinforces ideological norms that women should act and behave in a "ladylike" way.'
To what extent do you agree with this statement?

8 marks

The film is set in the 1930s, when expectations of how a woman should behave were different. 'Ladylike' behaviour may be to expect women to take care over their physical appearance, to defer to men, and to take a passive role. Several shots in the trailer reinforce this, for example:

Bear in mind that this film is set during a particular historical period, when expectations of female behaviour were different. However, the audience is still expected to react in a particular way to the plot and characters. Consider the following:
- The meaning of 'ladylike' in the context of the film.
- The contrast between Miss Pettigrew and Delysia.
- The ways in which both Miss Pettigrew and Delysia transgress accepted norms of female behaviour for the time, for example Miss Pettigrew smokes a cigar; Delysia is unmarried but sexually active.
- The preferred audience reading of Miss Pettigrew's makeover.

Now give some examples of how the film trailer subverts these expectations.

Conclude your answer, stating to what extent you agree with the statement.

Total for Question 4 = 20 marks

END OF GUIDED REVISION QUESTIONS

TOTAL FOR GUIDED REVISION QUESTIONS = 80 marks

Revision test 2

To support your revision, this Workbook contains revision tests to help you revise the skills that might be needed in your exam. The details of the actual exam may change so always make sure you are up to date. Ask your tutor or check the Pearson website for the most up-to-date Sample Assessment Material to get an idea of the structure of your exam and what this requires of you.

Answer ALL questions. Write your answers in the spaces provided.

1   Watch the video of the sitcom Outnumbered, available by scanning the QR code or entering the URL in your browser.

Watch the clip here

http://activetea.ch/2mJGvyZ

   (a)   Identify the type of camera positioning used at ten seconds into the clip.

`1 mark`

....

   (b)   Explain the purpose of this type of camera positioning.   `2 marks`

   Remember to refer to the clip to support the meaning of this type of camera positioning.

....

....

2   (a)   Explain **one** example of a stereotyped character in this episode.   `2 marks`

   You can choose any character who you think represents a stereotype, but you must provide appropriate examples from the clip of the episode to back up your ideas.

....

....

....

....

(b) Explain why the audience is likely to recognise the family in the show as a middle-class stereotype.

4 marks

....

....

....

....

....

....

....

3 Compare the representation of sisters Angela and Sue.

6 marks

Consider their appearance, their relationship with others in the clip, their attitudes and their portrayal of each other as they argue.

....

....

....

....

....

....

....

....

....

4 (a) Explain the effect of the continuity cut at 3.19–23 as Sue notices her daughter Karen in the kitchen. 2 marks

> Consider why this type of cut is used to draw attention to the implications of Karen overhearing the argument.

....

....

....

(b) Identify how Karen's innocence is contrasted with the anger shown by her mother and aunt in this clip. **4 marks**

> Think about props and costume as well as dialogue.

....

....

....

....

....

....

5 (a) Identify the type of shot that closes the sequence from 6.11. **1 mark**

....

(b) Explain why this type of shot has been used here. **1 mark**

> Think about the general function of this type of shot, and then consider why it might have been used at this point in the action.

....

....

6 Explain why low key lighting technique is used throughout this clip.

3 marks

Consider:
- the setting of a dinner party
- how the lighting affects the mood of the scene
- how it heightens the drama between the arguing sisters.

....

....

....

....

....

....

7 Explain ways in which this clip subverts typical conventions of the comedy genre.

6 marks

....

....

....

....

....

....

....

....

....

....

....

Links See page 14 of the Revision Guide for information about genre expectations and their subversion.

8 'The preferred reading of Pete's character is as a stressed but well-meaning husband and father.' Using examples from the episode, assess this statement.

6 marks

Remember that, in a preferred or dominant reading, the audience uncritically accepts and shares the meaning intended (consciously or subconsciously) by the producer. They respond in the way the producer expects them to and so confirm the social order. How do you think you are supposed to view Pete?

....

....

....

....

....

....

....

....

....

....

....

....

9 Analyse how an audience may read the combination of figure expression, dialogue and *mise-en-scène* in the scene from 1.42 to 2.53 to create meaning.　　**10 marks**

> Remember that the setting is a formal dinner party at which the hosts and the guests don't seem to know each other very well. Look for visual clues to their thoughts and how sound and dialogue are used within this awkward social situation.

....

....

....

....

....

....

....

....

....

....

....

....

....

....

....

....

....

....

10 '*Outnumbered* is a fictional representation of a family made in a documentary style.' To what extent do you agree with this statement?

12 marks

> Consider the conventions of a documentary that are unusual in the genre of a sitcom. These may include both technical aspects, such as camera positioning, and elements of dialogue and diegetic sound.

....

....

....

....

....

....

....

....

....

....

....

....

....

....

....

....

....

....

....

....

....

....

....

....

....

....

....

11 Evaluate the possible effects on society of media representations of family life. Use examples from this episode of *Outnumbered* to support your answer.

> Identify examples from the clip that reinforce, and oppose, ideological norms relating to families.
> Consider, for example:
> * gender roles
> * expectations of parental behaviour
> * the problems Sue and Pete face
> * ways in which their relationship can be viewed.

....

....

....

....

....

....

....

....

....

....

....

....

....

....

....

....

....

....

....

....

....

....

....

END OF REVISION QUESTIONS

TOTAL FOR REVISION QUESTIONS = 80 marks

Unit 3: Digital Media Skills

Your set task

Unit 3 will be assessed through a task, which will be set by Pearson. You will need to use your understanding of the creative digital media skills required to produce a product to a prescribed brief. You will also need to prepare appropriate documentation to demonstrate your creative and technical skills.

Your Revision Workbook

> This Workbook is designed to **revise skills** that might be needed in your assessed task. Ask your tutor or check the **Pearson website** for the most up-to-date **Sample Assessment Material** and **Mark Scheme** to get an indication of the structure of your assessed task and what this requires of you. The details of the actual assessed task may change so always make sure you are up to date.

To support your revision, this Workbook contains a revision task to help you revise the skills that might be needed in your assessed task.

You will revise your digital media skills in producing and documenting a product to a prescribed brief as you focus on the areas described below.

Reading the briefs

You will start by reading a task brief and understanding what it requires of you. You are then provided with five media briefs to choose from, depending on the medium you would wish to work in. You will use your skills to:
- identify the skills and equipment you would need to complete a each of the media briefs
- begin to think about the type of media product you could create to meet the given task brief.

Generating ideas and logging assets

For your chosen medium, you will then use your skills to consider how you would:
- generate ideas for a digital media product in response to a brief
- identify assets you could create and/or source for a digital media product
- record details of assets you would use in the creation of a digital media product.

Preparing assets and providing evidence

For your chosen medium, you will then use your skills to consider how you would:
- prepare, edit and manipulate assets for a media product
- record how and why you would edit and manipulate assets.

Creating and storing your media product

For your chosen medium, you will then use your skills to consider how you would:
- undertake the stages and techniques involved in building a final media product
- justify decisions and revisions in relation to a brief.

> **Links** To help you revise skills that might be needed in your Unit 3 set task, this Workbook contains a set of revision activities for five different types of media product. Depending on the medium you choose, you will find revision activities on the following pages:
> - video product – pages 27, 38 and 49
> - audio product – pages 29, 40 and 51
> - website – pages 31, 42 and 53
> - digital e-magazine – pages 33, 44 and 55
> - digital game – pages 35, 46 and 57.
>
> See the Introduction on page iii for more information on features included to help you revise.

Revision task

To support your revision, this Workbook contains a revision task to help you revise the skills that might be needed in your assessed task. The details of the actual assessed task may change so always make sure you are up to date. Ask your tutor or check the Pearson website for the most up-to-date Sample Assessment Material to get an idea of the structure of your assessed task and what this requires of you.

Revision task brief

Read the task brief below. You will need to refer back to this information when working your way through the activities in the following pages.

Your Finances

You have been commissioned to produce material for a new social media project, 'Your Finances'.

Your Finances will provide young people with support and guidance on financial matters. The project is aimed at young people planning to go on to higher education or enter work. It is intended to promote financial responsibility, and to provide relevant advice on issues such as:

- opening and managing a bank account
- managing loans and credit cards
- keeping personal data secure.

Your task is to create a digital media product that can be delivered as part of the Your Finances project. Your product can address a combination of the above topics, or any other relevant financial issue. It can be in any style or genre but it must be relevant and sustain the interest of an older teenage or young adult audience.

You must choose which medium you will use to create your media product and begin creating, sourcing and preparing the materials you will need. You may choose one brief from the five briefs on pages 21–25.

When you have read the task brief, answer these questions to help you to analyse it, and then choose your media brief.

1. What is the target audience for your product?

....

2. Use the internet to identify three key facts about personal bank accounts that you might want to communicate in a digital product.

   1 ....

   2 ....

   3 ....

3. Identify two other financial issues which might be relevant to teenagers or young adults.

   1 ....

   2 ....

4. What security issues might someone have to consider when dealing with their finances?

....

5. Use the internet to identify three key facts about how to keep your finances secure.

   1 ....

   2 ....

   3 ....

You only need to choose **one** media brief. Read the briefs on this page and pages 22–25 before deciding. Then read your chosen brief in detail and answer the questions about it.

Revision media brief 1: video product

If you have chosen the video product brief, read the brief below. Then answer the questions to help you consider what would be needed if taking the brief forward.

In order to complete your contribution to Your Finances, you will need to undertake the necessary preparation that will allow you to create your proposed product. You will need to gather and/or make appropriate assets for use in your video product, which should be no more than two minutes long. You will need to include:

- original footage with a variety of camera framing, angles and movement
- appropriate lighting
- an appropriate soundtrack
- appropriate editing techniques
- appropriate effects, titles and credits.

1. Make a skills checklist to identify the skills you would need to complete the brief.

Tick	Skill
	Creating a storyboard
	Lighting a video scene
	Recording raw video footage
	Recording wild track – audio
	Recording interview – audio
	Using editing software
	Creating titles and credits
	Syncing audio and video
	Rendering and transcoding video

2. Make a list of the equipment and software you would need to complete this brief.

   1 Video camera

   2 ....

   3 ....

   4 ....

   5 ....

3. Write down three different types of video product you could create to meet this brief.

   1 Interviews with students on how they manage their finances

   2 ....

   3 ....

Links You can revise the skills needed for creating video products on pages 49–52 of the Revision Guide.

Now go to page 26 to consider how you would generate ideas and log assets.

Revision media brief 2: audio product

> If you have chosen the audio product brief, read the brief below. Then answer the questions to help you consider what would be needed if taking the brief forward.

In order to complete your contribution to Your Finances, you will need to undertake the necessary preparation that will allow you to create your proposed production. You will need to gather and/or make appropriate assets for use in your audio product, which should be no more than two minutes long. You will need to include:

- your own recorded material
- appropriate microphone/recording techniques
- audio from sourced material
- appropriate editing techniques
- appropriate effects and transitions.

⟩ Guided ⟩ 1. Make a skills checklist to identify the skills you would need to complete the brief.

Tick	Skill
	Recording audio material
	Recording interview(s)
	Recording wild track
	Creating a script
	Using editing software
	Creating cue sheets
	Creating audio titles and credits
	Mixing down

2. Make a list of the equipment and software you would need to complete this brief.

   1 Portable recorder

   2 ....

   3 ....

   4 ....

   5 ....

3. Write down three different types of audio product you could create to meet this brief.

   1 A music-based programme with segments of financial advice

   2 ....

   3 ....

 You can revise the skills needed for creating audio products on pages 53–55 of the Revision Guide.

Now go to page 26 to consider how you would generate ideas and log assets.

Revision media brief 3: website

If you have chosen the website brief, read the brief below. Then answer the questions to help you consider what would be needed if taking the brief forward.

In order to complete your contribution to Your Finances, you will need to undertake the necessary preparation that will allow you to create your proposed product. You will need to gather and/or make appropriate assets for use on your website. You will need to include:

- a consistent page layout and design
- your own original graphics
- images from sourced material that have been edited and optimised
- interactivity
- appropriate accessibility features.

 Guided

1. Make a skills checklist to identify the skills you would need to complete the brief.

Tick	Skill
	Creating your own layout and design
	Creating your own digital graphics
	Finding sourced material
	Editing and optimising sourced material
	Creating interactivity
	Combing images, text and graphics
	Creating appropriate accessibility features

2. Find two examples of financial websites and use them to describe an example of:

   1 graphics or animations

   ....

   ....

   2 interactivity

   ....

   ....

3. Describe three features that would make the website attractive to the target audience.

   1 A web page on keeping personal data secure using colourful and engaging graphics

   2 ....

   3 ....

 Links You can revise the skills needed for creating web products on pages 60–63 of the Revision Guide.

Now go to page 26 to consider how you would generate ideas and log assets.

Revision media brief 4: digital e-magazine

If you have chosen the digital e-magazine brief, read the brief below. Then answer the questions to help you consider what would be needed if taking the brief forward.

In order to complete your contribution to Your Finances, you will need to undertake the necessary preparation that will allow you to create your proposed product. You will need to gather and/or make appropriate assets for use in your digital e-magazine. You will need to include:

- a consistent page layout and design
- your own original photography and copy
- audiovisual material from sourced material
- interactivity
- appropriate images and graphics.

Guided

1. Make a skills checklist to identify the skills you would need to complete the brief.

Tick	Skill
	Creating your own photographs
	Creating your own copy
	Finding audiovisual sourced material
	Creating interactivity
	Creating appropriate graphics
	Creating appropriate images

2. Make a list of the equipment and software you would need to complete this brief.

   1 Digital camera

   2 ....

   3 ....

   4 ....

   5 ....

3. Write down three different types of e-magazine content you could create to meet the needs of this brief.

   1 An interactive quiz on how to set up a bank account

   2 ....

   3 ....

Links You can revise the skills needed for creating digital print products on pages 56–59 of the Revision Guide.

Now go to page 26 to consider how you would generate ideas and log assets.

Revision media brief 5: digital game

If you have chosen the digital game brief, read the brief below. Then answer the questions to help you consider what would be needed if taking the brief forward.

In order to complete your contribution to Your Finances, you will need to undertake the necessary preparation that will allow you to create your proposed digital game. You will need to gather and/or make appropriate assets for use in your digital game, which must contain at least two levels. You will need to include:

- rules and rewards
- interactivity
- your own original assets
- an appropriate soundtrack
- assets from sourced material.

Guided

1. Make a skills checklist to identify the skills you would need to complete the brief.

Tick	Skill
	Developing original game ideas
	Creating rules and rewards
	Creating interactivity
	Developing characters
	Developing environments
	Creating an appropriate soundtrack
	Developing assets from secondary sources

2. Make a list of the equipment and software you would need to complete this brief.

1 A games engine

2 ....

3 ....

4 ....

5 ....

3. Write down three different types of game you could create to meet the requirements of the brief.

1 A reward game where points are given for making personal data secure

2 ....

3 ....

 Links You can revise the skills needed for creating a digital game on pages 64–69 of the Revision Guide.

Now go to page 26 to consider how you would generate ideas and log assets.

Generating ideas and logging assets

Guided

Once you have selected which media brief you would want to use, you need to generate ideas for your product, create or source assets for it, and provide evidence of the creation (or source) of those assets and their relevance to the brief.

- For any assets that you might create, you need to provide evidence of how this was achieved.
- For any sourced assets, you need to provide evidence of the source and the processes involved in sourcing the assets, and explain their relevance to the product.
- All your assets should be saved in an appropriate format and organised in a logical way.

Here are some examples of assets you could gather if you were following **Media brief 3** and creating a website along with examples of appropriate filenames and clear notes on how the assets relate to the brief. It is important to save any created assets using filenames that make it easy to identify them.

Created material: MONEY_ICONS.png

Evidence: I created these vector graphics icons using Adobe Illustrator. My original working file is contained within the folder with the filename MONEY_ICONS.AI.

Relevance: Using these icons as buttons or bullets will strongly associate my website with its financial theme.

This revision task will help you revise the skills that might be needed in your assessed task. The details of the actual assessed task may change so always make sure you are up to date. Ask your tutor or check the Pearson website for the most up-to-date Sample Assessment Material to get an idea of the structure of your assessed task and what this requires of you.

Sourced material: ONLINE_BANKING_PHOTO.jpg

Evidence: This image was sourced from a free online photo library.

Relevance: I intend to use this as a hero image on the page of my site dedicated to online banking security and the importance of keeping your PIN safe.

Links Go to the following pages to find the activities related to your chosen media brief:
- Video product – page 27
- Audio product – page 29
- Website – page 31
- Digital e-magazine – page 33
- Digital game – page 35

Guided

If you chose **Media brief 1 (video product)**, use this page to help you consider the generation of ideas and logging assets.

1. Complete this mind map of ideas for **created material** you could produce for this brief.

Interviews with bank staff about how bank accounts work

B-roll of young person at an ATM using correct safety measures, e.g. shielding their pin number

Created material

2. Write down ideas for **sourced material** you could find for this brief.

....

....

....

....

....

....

....

3. (a) List **three** possible interviewees that you know or could contact who could be involved in the product.

   1 ....

   2 ....

   3 ....

   (b) Write a short email to a local bank manager asking if they would be happy to talk to you on camera.

   ....

   ....

   ....

   ....

   ....

   ....

   ....

   ....

   ....

   ....

   ....

....
....
....
....
....
....
....
....
....

4. Choose one piece of video footage that you could to create for the product. Create a short storyboard for it. Create your storyboard on separate paper or using a computer.

5. Write a short log entry for the piece of video footage you storyboarded in question 4, noting how you would create it and its relevance to the product.

Filename	
Length	
Shoot date(s)	
Evidence of creation	This footage was shot using
Relevance to product	This footage will be relevant to my product because

If you were completing this activity for your finished product, you would need to:
• create a log entry for every asset, showing evidence of how it was sourced and its relevance
• save all your assets in an appropriately named folder, using sensible filenames and file structure.

Now go to page 37 to consider how you would prepare assets and provide evidence.

If you chose **Media brief 2 (audio product)**, use this page to help you consider the generation of ideas and logging assets.

> **Guided**

1. Complete this mind map of ideas for **created material** you could produce for this brief.

Interviews with students about how they control their finances

Information from a financial consultant about keeping personal data safe, e.g. PINs, online security

Created material

Sound recording of bank telling machines counting money

2. Write down ideas for **sourced material** you could find for this brief.

....

....

....

....

....

....

3. (a) List **three** possible interviewees that you know or could contact who could be involved in the product.

1 ....

2 ....

3 ....

(b) Write a short email to a local bank manager asking if they would be happy to talk to you on audio.

....

....

....

....

....

....

....

....

....

....

....

....

....

....

....

....

4. Choose one piece of audio material that you could create for the product. Write a short script for it. Write your script on separate paper or using a computer.

5. Write a short log entry for the piece of audio material you scripted in question 4, noting how you would have created it and its relevance to the product.

Filename	
Length	
Recording date(s)	
Evidence of creation	This audio material was recorded using
Relevance to product	This audio material will be relevant to my product because

If you were completing this activity for your finished product you would need to:
• create a log entry for every asset, showing evidence of how it was sourced and its relevance
• save all your assets in an appropriately named folder using sensible filenames and file structure.

Now go to page 37 to consider how you would prepare assets and provide evidence.

If you chose **Media brief 3 (website)**, use this page to help you consider generation of ideas and logging assets.

1. Complete this mind map of ideas for **created material** you could produce for this brief.

A quiz web page on how to open a bank account

A page with advice from existing students on how to manage your money

Created material

Digital photographs of ATM operation

2. Write down ideas for **sourced material** you could find for this brief.

....

....

....

....

....

....

....

3. (a) List **three** possible interviewees that you know or could contact who could be involved in the product.

   1 ....

   2 ....

   3 ....

   (b) Write a short email to a local bank manager asking if they would be happy to talk to you for the website.

....

....

....

....

....

....

....

....

....

....

....

....

....

....

....

....

4. Choose one digital graphic that you could create for the product. Create a design layout for it. You could sketch your layout on a separate page, or use suitable computer software.

5. Write a short log entry for the digital graphic you created a design layout for in question 4, noting how you would have created it and its relevance to the product.

Filename	
Length	
Creation date(s)	
Evidence of creation	This graphic was made using
Relevance to product	This digital graphic will be relevant to my product because

If you were creating this activity for your finished product, you would need to:
• create a log entry for every asset, showing evidence of how it was sourced and its relevance
• save all your assets in an appropriately named folder using sensible filenames and file structure.

Now go to page 37 to consider how you would prepare assets and provide evidence.

Guided

If you chose **Media brief 4 (digital e-magazine)**, use this page to help you consider generation of ideas and logging assets.

1. Complete this mind map of ideas for **created material** you could produce for this brief.

An interactive quiz on keeping your personal data safe

An article on opening a bank account with short video insert from a bank manager

Created material

Digital shots of teller processing payment

2. Write down ideas for **sourced material** you could find for this brief.

....

....

....

....

....

....

....

3. (a) List **three** possible interviewees that you know or could contact who could be involved in the product.

1 ....

2 ....

3 ....

(b) Write a short email to a local bank manager asking if they would talk to you on camera or audio.

....

....

....

....

....

....

....

....

....

....

....

....

....

....

....

....

4. Choose one original photograph that you could create for the product. Create a page layout and caption for it, using a suitable software package, or on a separate sheet of paper.

5. Write a short log entry for the original photograph you created a layout for and captioned in question 4, noting how you would have created it and its relevance to the product.

Filename	
Size	
Shoot date(s)	
Evidence of creation	This photograph was shot using
Relevance to product	This photograph will be relevant to my product because

If you were completing this activity for your finished product, you would need to:
• create a log entry for every asset, showing evidence of how it was sourced and its relevance
• save all your assets in an appropriately named folder, using sensible filenames and file structure.

Now go to page 37 to consider how you would prepare assets and provide evidence.

If you chose **Media brief 5 (digital game)**, use this page to help you consider generation of ideas and logging assets.

Guided >

1. Complete this mind map of ideas for **created material** you could produce for this brief.

An environment of a bank with rewards for correct opening of an account, e.g. taking identification

A character-based task level on keeping financial data safe

Created material

2. Write down ideas for **sourced material** you could find for this brief.

....

....

....

....

....

....

....

3. (a) List **three** possible interviewees that you know or could contact who could be involved in the product.

1 ....

2 ....

3 ....

(b) Write a short email to a local bank manager asking if they could talk to you about online banking security.

....

....

....

....

....

....

....

....

....

....

....

....

....

....

....

....

4. Choose one character that you could create for the digital game. Create a gender identity and develop the role the character plays in the digital game. You should do this on separate paper or using a computer.

5. Write a short log entry for the character you created an identity for and developed in question 4, noting how you would have created it and its relevance to the product.

Filename	
Size	
Creation date(s)	
Evidence of creation	This character was created using
Relevance to product	This character will be relevant to my product because

If completing this activity for your finished product you would need to:
• create a log entry for every asset, showing evidence of how it was sourced and its relevance
• save all your assets in an appropriately named folder using sensible filenames and file structure.

Now go to page 37 to consider how you would prepare assets and provide evidence.

Preparing assets and providing evidence

Once you have planned, sourced, annotated, logged and stored any assets you might create or want to use, you need to prepare them for use in your product. You also need to provide evidence of your work and justify your decisions.

Using your created and/or sourced assets you need to:

* prepare, edit and manipulate these assets for the product, demonstrating a comprehensive understanding and skilled application of the processes involved
* write detailed and accurate annotations for the assets, fully justifying your editing/manipulation decisions in relation to the brief.

Here is an example of a manipulation you could make if you were following **Media brief 4** and creating a digital e-magazine. You would need to write a commentary describing all your alterations, and show evidence of any processes you have used.

Guided

Source image 1

BLANK_PHONE.jpg

Source image 2

PHONE_SCREEN_MOCK.jpg

Final manipulated image

MOBILE_BANK.psd

Software used: Photoshop

Description: I wanted to create an image to demonstrate mobile banking. I used a photograph of my phone while it was switched off, and created a mocked-up phone screen. I wanted to remove the distracting background so I used the Quick Select and Magic Wand tools to select the phone and hand to create a layer mask. I used the Feather and Smooth tools to make sure my selection did not have any artefacts. I then imported the mocked-up screen and sized it to fit the screen of my phone in the photo, before adding a bevel effect to create the illusion of a border.

This revision task will help you revise the skills that might be needed in your assessed task. The details of the actual assessed task may change so always make sure you are up to date. Ask your tutor or check the Pearson website for the most up-to-date Sample Assessment Material to get an idea of the structure of your assessed task and what this requires of you.

 Links Go to the following pages to find the activities related to your chosen media brief:

* Video product – page 38
* Audio product – page 40
* Website – page 42

* Digital e-magazine – page 44
* Digital game – page 46

If you chose **Media brief 1 (video product)**, use this page to help you consider the choices and skills involved in preparing assets and providing evidence.

Think about a video product you have already worked on and any video assets you have edited or manipulated for it, and answer the questions below.

1. Choose one scene from your video and describe how you changed, or could have changed, the colour balance for that scene.

....

....

....

....

....

2. Describe how you edited another piece of footage to make it appropriate for your finished video.

....

....

....

....

3. Describe how you changed the sound balance in your video.

....

....

....

....

4. Describe how you created the titles and credits for your video.

....

....

....

....

....

5. Choosing one of your assets, describe how and why this asset changed.

....

....

....

....

....

6. Describe how you annotated your manipulations and editing, such as by using screen grabs, sticky notes and/or commentaries.

....

....

....

....

....

7. Now consider the task brief for Your Finances on page 20. If you were working on a video product for this brief, think of an example of the type of editing/manipulation process you would need to undertake for one of the assets you might create. Think about what you might do, how you would do it and why (look at the example again on page 37 to help you).

....

....

....

....

....

If you were completing this activity for your finished product, you would need to:
• carry out any manipulations you need to make to your assets
• create a log entry for every asset, explaining the alterations you made.

Now go to page 48 to consider how you would create and store your media product.

If you chose **Media brief 2 (audio product)**, use this page to help you consider the choices and skills involved in preparing assets and providing evidence.

Think about an audio product you have already worked on and any audio assets you have edited or manipulated for it, and answer the questions below.

1. Choose one interview and describe how you changed, or could have changed, the sound balance for that interview.

....

....

....

....

....

2. Describe how you edited a different scene of recorded material to make it appropriate for your finished audio product.

....

....

....

....

....

3. Describe how you changed the balance of voice and sound effects in your audio product.

....

....

....

....

....

4. Describe how you created the titles and credits for your audio product.

....

....

....

....

....

5. Describe how you checked that your audio product was stored safely and in the correct file format.

....

....

....

....

....

6. Describe how you annotated your manipulations and editing, such as by using screen grabs, sticky notes and/or commentaries.

....

....

....

....

....

7. Now consider the task brief for Your Finances on page 20. If you were working on an audio product for this brief, think of an example of the type of editing/manipulation process you would need to undertake for one of the assets you might create. Think about what you might do, how you would do it and why (look at the example again on page 37 to help you).

....

....

....

....

....

If you were completing this activity for your finished product, you would need to:
• carry out any manipulations you need to make to your assets
• create a log entry for every asset, explaining the alterations you made.

Now go to page 48 to consider how you would create and store your media product.

If you chose **Media brief 3 (website)**, use this page to help you consider the choices and skills involved in preparing assets and providing evidence.

Think about a website product you have already worked on, and any graphic and textual assets you have edited or manipulated for it, and answer the questions below.

1. Choose one of your graphic designs and describe how you changed it, or could have changed it, to work effectively on your website.

....

....

....

....

....

2. Choosing another graphic design, describe how you changed, or could have changed, its colour to fit in with the rest of your website.

....

....

....

....

....

3. Describe how you changed the text you created to make it appropriate for use in your website.

....

....

....

....

....

4. Describe how you changed your text, images and graphics to produce appropriate interactivity.

....

....

....

....

5. Describe how you checked that your website was stored safely and in the correct file format.

....

....

....

....

....

6. Describe how you annotated your manipulations and editing, such as by using screen grabs, sticky notes and/or commentaries.

....

....

....

....

....

7. Now consider the task brief for Your Finances on page 20. If you were working on a website product for this brief, think of an example of the type of editing/manipulation process you would need to undertake for one of the assets you might create. Think about what you might do, how you would do it and why (look at the example again on page 37 to help you).

....

....

....

....

....

If you were completing this activity for your finished product, you would need to:
- carry out any manipulations you need to make to your assets
- create a log entry for every asset, explaining the alterations you made.

Now go to page 48 to consider how you would create and store your media product.

If you chose **Media brief 4 (digital e-magazine)**, use this page to help you consider the choices and skills involved in preparing assets and providing evidence.

Think about a digital e-magazine product you have already worked on, and any digital images, graphics and copy you have edited or manipulated for it, and answer the questions below.

1. Choose one of your digital images and describe how you changed it, or could have changed it, to work effectively in your digital e-magazine.

....

....

....

....

2. Choose one of your digital graphics and describe how you changed it, or could have changed it, to work effectively in your digital e-magazine.

....

....

....

....

....

3. Describe how you changed the copy you created to make it appropriate for use in your digital e-magazine.

....

....

....

....

4. Describe how you changed your copy, images and graphics to produce appropriate interactivity in your digital e-magazine.

....

....

....

....

....

5. Describe how you changed your copy, images and graphics to make them combine effectively in your digital e-magazine.

....

....

....

....

....

6. Describe how you annotated your manipulations and editing, such as by using screen grabs, sticky notes and/or commentaries.

....

....

....

....

....

7. Now consider the task brief for Your Finances on page 20. If you were working on a digital e-magazine product for this brief, think of an example of the type of editing/manipulation process you would need to undertake for one of the assets you might create. Think about what you might do, how you would do it and why (look at the example again on page 37 to help you).

....

....

....

....

....

If you were completing this activity for your finished product, you would need to:
• carry out any manipulations you need to make to your assets
• create a log entry for every asset, explaining the alterations you made.

Now go to page 48 to consider how you would create and store your media product.

If you chose **Media brief 5 (digital game)**, use this page to help you consider the choices and skills involved in preparing assets and providing evidence.

Think about a digital game product you have already worked on and any characters, environments and soundtrack assets you have edited or manipulated for it, and answer the questions below.

1. Describe how you changed one of your characters to make them work effectively in your digital game.

....

....

....

....

....

2. Choose one of your environments and describe how you changed it to make it work effectively in your digital game.

....

....

....

....

....

3. Describe how you combined your characters and environment(s).

....

....

....

....

....

4. Describe how you changed, or could have changed, your soundtrack to fit with your characters and environment in one level.

....

....

....

....

....

5. Describe how you changed, or could have changed, one of your sourced material ideas to make it work in your digital game.

....

....

....

....

6. Describe how you annotated your manipulations and editing, such as by using screen grabs, sticky notes and/or commentaries.

....

....

....

....

7. Now consider the task brief for Your Finances on page 20. If you were working on a digital game product for this brief, think of an example of the type of editing/manipulation process you would need to undertake for one of the assets you might create. Think about what you might do, how you would do it and why (look at the example again on page 37 to help you).

....

....

....

....

....

If you were completing this activity for your finished product, you would need to:
• carry out any manipulations you need to make to your assets
• create a log entry for every asset, explaining the alterations you made.

Now go to page 48 to consider how you would create and store your media product.

Creating and storing your media product

Once you have completed your preparation, editing and manipulation of the assets, you would need to create the final media product.

Using your prepared, edited and manipulated assets you would need to consider:
- how you show your understanding of the application of techniques used in the building/creating of a media product
- how you show your detailed development of the build/creation process, with the components in the build/creation present, appropriate and in place
- how you safely save the media product
- how the media product meets the brief, showing your creativity.

Here is an example of a website page you could have made if you were following **Media brief 3 (website)**. An example is also given of the learner's creative thinking behind their ideas for this website page and one other to contribute to the fulfillment of the brief, and a record of the software they used and how they stored their pages, which contributes to demonstrating the technical skills they used in creating their website.

 Guided

You and your money quiz

What is the quiz all about?
This is a fun quiz to find out how people think about their money and how they manage their finances. It is designed to be used in a group situation and allows you to see how people behave around money issues.

What will I need?
- Prepared quiz screen
- Answer sheets
- Pens

How will I manage the quiz?
1. Divide the room into equal groups.
2. Ensure that each group has an answer sheet and a volunteer to write down their answers.
3. Make sure that everyone can see the screen to read the questions.
4. Go through each question in turn and ask that answers are put on the answer sheet.
5. Pick one group to share their answers with the entire room.
6. Encourage an entire-group discussion on the answers.

(Time for the quiz – 15 minutes)

How are you with money? Quiz questions
1. How do you keep your PIN numbers safe?
2. Where do you keep your cheque book and/or credit cards?
3. What would you do if you lost your credit or debit card?
4. What are the rules for reporting lost or stolen cards?
5. Is it safe to keep money 'under your mattress'?
6. Where would you go for advice on a savings account?
7. Where would you look for the best price, for example, for a mobile phone?
8. How often do you check your bank or credit card account for fraudulent activities?

Software used: WebPlus X8

Description: I used WebPlus X8 software to create this page of my website. I thought that it would be good to use a quiz so that young people can go through these questions and see how good they are with money. I then created another page to help them with opening and managing a bank account. I used an interview with a bank manager to help with this. I wanted to keep my audience engaged so I included both funny and serious content. I stored my website in .html format.

Links Go to the following pages to find the activities related to your chosen brief:
- Video product – page 49
- Audio product – page 51
- Website – page 53
- Digital e-magazine – page 55
- Digital game – page 57

This revision task will help you revise the skills that might be needed in your assessed task. The details of the actual assessed task may change so always make sure you are up to date. Ask your tutor or check the Pearson website for the most up-to-date Sample Assessment Material to get an idea of the structure of your assessed task and what this requires of you.

If you chose **Media brief 1 (video product)**, use this page to help you consider the choices and skills involved in creating and storing your media product.

Think about a video product you have already worked on, along with the brief for Your Finances, and answer the questions below.

1. You need to collect together all your assets and ensure you have everything you would need to complete your video. Give an example of how you would list a selection of your assets, their filenames and where you would store them.

Asset description	Filename	Stored

2. Make a checklist of the stages you would go through when creating your video product.

Tick	Stage and description

3. Make a production schedule or diary so that you know when you would have to finish your work on your video product. Remember to identify a date when you can test your product.

....
....
....
....
....
....
....
....
....
....
....
....
....
....

4. Describe the kind of changes you might need to consider making to your video product when testing has been completed, such as re-editing scenes for length.

....

....

....

....

....

5. What should you consider to ensure that your media product meets the requirements of the brief? For example, length, standards, fitness for purpose.

....

....

....

....

....

If you were going to complete this activity for your finished product, you would need to:
• collate all your assets for your video product
• create your video product.

You have now completed your revision task.

If you chose **Media brief 2 (audio product)**, use this page to help you consider the choices and skills involved in creating and storing your media product.

Think about an audio product you have already worked on, alongside the brief for Your Finances, and answer the questions below.

 1. You need to collect together all your assets and ensure you have everything you need to complete your audio product. Give an example of how you would list a selection of your assets, their filenames and where you would store them.

Asset description	Filename	Stored

2. Make a checklist of the stages you would go through when creating your audio product.

Tick	Stage and description

3. Make a production schedule or diary so that you know when you would have to finish your work on your audio product. Remember to identify a date when you can test your product.

....
....
....
....
....
....
....
....
....
....
....
....
....

4. Describe the kind of changes you might need to consider making to your audio product when testing has been completed, such as remixing sound levels.

....

....

....

....

5. What should you consider to ensure that your media product meets the requirements of the brief? For example, length, standards, fitness for purpose.

....

....

....

....

....

If you were going to complete this activity for your finished product, you need to:
• collate all your assets for your audio product
• create your audio product.

You have now completed your revision task.

If you chose **Media brief 3 (website)**, use this page to help you consider the choices and skills involved in creating and storing your media product.

Think about a website product you have already worked on, alongside the brief for Your Finances, and answer the questions below.

1. You need to collect together all your assets and ensure you have everything you need to complete your website. Give an example of how you would list a selection of your assets, their filenames and where you would store them.

Asset description	Filename	Stored

2. Make a checklist of the stages you would go through when creating your website.

Tick	Stage and description

3. Make a production schedule or diary so that you know when you would have to finish your work on your website. Remember to identify a date when you can test your product.

....

....

....

....

....

....

....

....

....

....

....

....

....

4. Describe the kind of changes you might need to consider making to your website when testing has been completed, such as reworking graphics, considering readability.

....

....

....

....

....

5. What should you consider to ensure that your media product meets the requirements of the brief? For example, length, standards, fitness for purpose.

....

....

....

....

....

If you were going to complete this activity for your finished product, you would need to:
• collate all your assets for your website
• create your website.

You have now completed your revision task.

If you chose **Media brief 4 (digital e-magazine)**, use this page to help you consider the choices and skills involved in creating and storing your media product.

Think about a digital e-magazine product you have already worked on, alongside the brief for Your Finances, and answer the questions below.

1. You need to collect together all your assets and ensure you have everything you need to complete your digital e-magazine. Give an example of how you would list a selection of your assets, their filenames and where you would store them.

Asset description	Filename	Stored

2. Make a checklist of the stages you would go through when creating your digital e-magazine.

Tick	Stage and description

3. Make a production schedule or diary so that you know when you would have to finish your work on your digital e-magazine. Remember to identify a date when you can test your product.

....

....

....

....

....

....

....

....

....

....

....

....

....

4. Describe the kind of changes you might need to consider making to your digital e-magazine when testing has been completed, such as rewriting copy, reshooting images.

....

....

....

....

....

5. What should you consider to ensure that your media product meets the requirements of the brief? For example, length, standards, fitness for purpose.

....

....

....

....

....

If you were going to complete this activity for your finished product, you would need to:
• collate all your assets for your digital e-magazine
• create your digital e-magazine.

You have now completed your revision task.

If you chose **Media brief 5 (digital game)**, use this page to help you consider the choices and skills involved in creating and storing your media product.

Think about a digital game product you have already worked on, alongside the brief for Your Finances, and answer the questions below.

1. You need to collect together all your assets and ensure you have everything you need to complete your digital game. Give an example of how you would list a selection of your assets, their filenames and where you would store them.

Asset description	Filename	Stored

2. Make a checklist of the stages you would go through when creating your digital game.

Tick	Stage and description

3. Make a production schedule or diary so that you know when you would have to finish your work on your digital game. Remember to identify a date when you can test your product.

....

....

....

....

....

....

....

....

....

....

....

....

....

....

4. Describe the kind of changes you might need to consider making to your digital game when testing has been completed, such as changing the nature of a character.

    ....

    ....

    ....

    ....

    ....

5. What should you consider to ensure that your media product meets the requirements of the brief? For example, length, standards, fitness for purpose.

    ....

    ....

    ....

    ....

    ....

If you were going to complete this activity for your finished product, you would need to:
- collate all your assets for your digital game
- create your digital game.

You have now completed the revision task. When creating a media product you need to consider:
- how you show your understanding of the application of techniques used in the building/creating of a media product
- how you show your detailed development of the build/creation process, with the components in the build/creation present, appropriate and in place
- how the media product meets the brief, showing your creativity.

END OF REVISION TASK

Unit 5: Specialist Subject Investigation

Your set task

Unit 5 will be assessed through a task, which will be set by Pearson. You will need to use your understanding of research methods and techniques related to a piece of stimulus material on a media issue or debate, along with your own skills in carrying out both primary and secondary research around the issue or debate. You then answer questions based on your research.

Your Revision Workbook

This Workbook is designed to **revise skills** that might be needed in your assessed task. The selected content, outcomes, questions and answers are provided to help you to revise content and ways of applying your skills. Ask your tutor or check the **Pearson website** for the most up-to-date **Sample Assessment Material** to get an indication of the structure of your assessed task and what this requires of you. The details of the actual assessed task may change so always make sure you are up to date.

To support your revision, this Workbook contains revision tasks to help you revise the skills that might be needed in your assessed task. Each revision task is divided into two sections:

1 Research

In your Workbook you will use your skills to:
- read, analyse and make notes on a piece of stimulus material (pages 67–68 and pages 87–88)
- plan your own independent primary and secondary research related to the media issue or debate you identify, relating your research to a specific media sector (pages 69 and 88)
- carry out your research and make notes on it (pages 70–71 and 89–92)
- prepare a catalogue of your sources (pages 72 and 93).

2 Revision activities

Your response to the activities will help you to revise:
- understanding of research methods and how to interpret data (pages 73–74 and 94)
- evaluating research findings and conclusions (pages 75 and 95)
- identifying and explaining the impact of the media topic on media production (pages 76 and 96)
- identifying and explaining the impact of the media topic on media consumption (pages 77 and 97)
- making research recommendations (pages 78 and 98).

Links To help you revise skills that might be needed in your Unit 5 set task, this Workbook contains two revision tasks, starting on pages 60 and 79. The first is guided and models good techniques, to help you develop your skills. The second gives you the opportunity to apply the skills you have developed. See the Introduction on page iii for more information on features included to help you revise.

Revision task 1

To support your revision, this Workbook contains revision tasks to help you revise the skills that might be needed in your assessed task. The details of the actual assessed task may change so always make sure you are up to date. Ask your tutor or check the Pearson website for the most up-to-date Sample Assessment Material to get an idea of the structure of your assessed task and what this requires of you.

Read the article below. There are revision activities to support your research from page 67 onwards.

Task information

Revision Task Information

Stimulus material – article

Ofcom (2008): *Social Networking: A quantitative and qualitative research report into attitudes, behaviours and use.*

The following are edited extracts from this report.

Introduction/executive summary

The rapid growth of social networking over the last two to three years is indicative of its entry into mainstream culture and its integration into the daily lives of many people. There has also been considerable media coverage of the growth of social networking, its potential positive outcomes and concerns about the way that some people are engaging with it.

Social networking sites offer people new and varied ways to communicate via the internet, whether through their PC or mobile phone. Examples include MySpace, Facebook and Bebo. They allow people to create their own online page or profile easily and simply and to construct and display an online network of contacts, often called 'friends'. Users of these sites can communicate via their profile both with their 'friends' and with people outside their list of contacts. This can be on a one-to-one basis (much like an email), or in a more public way such as a comment posted for all to see.

The rapid growth of social networking sites in recent years indicates that they are now a mainstream communications technology for many people.

Summary of key themes

Social networking sites are most popular with teenagers and young adults

Ofcom research shows that just over one-fifth (22%) of adult internet users aged 16+ and almost half (49%) of children aged 8–17* who use the internet have set up their own profile on a social networking site. For adults, the likelihood of setting up a profile is highest among 16–24-year-olds (54%) and decreases with age.

*The report uses the term 'children' to include all people aged 8–17. For the 'Adult Media Literacy Audit' (2008), 16- and 17-year-olds are classed as adults, but as children for the 'Children, Young People and Online Content research' (October 2007).

Some under-13s are bypassing the age restrictions on social networking sites

Although the minimum age for most social networking sites is usually 13 (14 on MySpace), 27% of 8–11-year-olds who are aware of social networking sites say that they have a profile. While some of these users are on sites intended for children of their age, the presence of underage users on social networking sites intended for those aged 13 or over is also confirmed by qualitative research conducted by Ofcom.

The average adult social networker has profiles on 1.6 sites, and most users check their profile at least every other day

Adult social networkers use a variety of sites, with the main ones being Bebo, Facebook and MySpace. It is common for adults to have a profile on more than one site – on average each adult with a social networking page or profile has profiles on 1.6 sites, and 39% of adults have profiles on 2 or more sites. Half of all current adult social networkers say that they access their profiles at least every other day.

The site chosen varies depending on the user. Children are more likely to use Bebo (63% of those who have a social networking site profile), and the most popular site for adults is Facebook (62% of those who have a social networking profile). There is also a difference between socio-economic groups: ABC1s with a social networking profile are more likely to use Facebook than C2DEs, who prefer MySpace.

Two-thirds of parents claim to set rules on their child's use of social networking sites, although only 53% of children say that their parents set such rules

The rules and restrictions that parents set on social networking site usage are an important influencing factor in the child's use of such sites. Two-thirds of parents whose children have a social networking page say they set rules on their child's use of these sites. Most commonly these concern meeting new people online and giving out personal details. However, significantly fewer children (53% of those with social networking profiles) say that their parents set rules on their use of these sites.

Social networkers fall into distinct groups

Social networkers differ in their attitudes to social networking sites and in their behaviour while using them. Ofcom's qualitative research indicates that site users tend to fall into five distinct groups based on their behaviours and attitudes. These are as follows:

○ **Alpha socialisers**: People who use sites in intense short bursts to flirt, meet new people and be entertained (a minority).

○ **Attention seekers**: People who crave attention and comments from others, often by posting photos and customising their profiles (some).

○ **Followers**: People who join sites to keep up with what their peers are doing (many).

○ **Faithfuls**: People who typically use social networking sites to rekindle old friendships, often from school or university (many).

○ **Functionals**: People who tend to be single-minded in using sites for a particular purpose (a minority).

Non-users of social networking sites also fall into distinct groups

Non-users also appear to fall into distinct groups, based on their reasons for not using social networking sites:

○ **Concerned about safety**: People concerned, in particular, about making personal details available online.

○ **Technically inexperienced**: People who lack confidence in using the internet and computers.

○ **Intellectual rejecters**: People with no interest in social networking sites who see them as a waste of time.

While communication with contacts is the most popular social networking activity, 17% of adults use their profile to communicate with people they do not know. This increases among younger adults

Both quantitative and qualitative research shows that communication is the most popular activity on social networking sites. Users communicate mainly with people with whom they have at least some form of pre-existing relationship. Some 69% of adults who have a social networking page or profile use social networking sites to talk to friends or family who they see regularly anyway, compared to 17% of adults who use sites to talk to those they don't already know. In particular, users of all ages see social networking sites as a means of managing existing relationships, and for getting back in contact with old friends.

Among those who report talking to people they don't know, there are significant variations in age, but those who talk to people they don't know are significantly more likely to be aged 16–24 (22% of those with a social networking page or profile) than 25–34 (7% of those with a profile). In our qualitative sample, several people report using sites in this way to look for romance.

Only a few users highlight negative aspects to social networking

Most comments in our qualitative sample are positive about social networking. A few users do mention negative aspects to social networking, such as annoyance at others using sites for self-promotion, parties organised online getting out of hand, and online bullying.

From Ofcom's qualitative research it appears that concerns about privacy and safety are not 'top of mind' for most users

The people who use social networking sites see them as a fun and easy leisure activity. Although the subject of much discussion in the media, in Ofcom's qualitative research, privacy and safety issues on social networking sites do not emerge as significant for most users. In discussion, and after prompting, some users do think of some privacy and safety issues, although on the whole they are unconcerned about them.

In addition, our qualitative study finds that all users, even those who are confident with ICT, find the settings on most of the major social networking sites difficult to understand and manipulate.

Several areas of potentially risky behaviour are suggested by the qualitative and/or quantitative research

These include:

- leaving privacy settings set to default 'open' (Ofcom Social Networking qualitative research). Among children aged 8–17 with a visible profile, 41% have their profile set so that it is visible to anyone (Children, young people and online content quantitative research). Among adults with a current profile, 44% say their profile can be seen by anyone (this is more likely among those aged 18–24) (Adult Media Literacy Audit 2008)

- giving out sensitive personal information, photographs and other content (Ofcom social networking sites research/Get Safe Online Report 2007). Our qualitative research finds that some users willingly give out sensitive personal information. This is supported by the Get Safe Online research which finds that 25% of registered social networking users have posted sensitive personal data about themselves on their profiles. This includes details such as their phone number, home address or email address. Younger adults are even more likely to do this, with 34% of 16–24-year-olds willingly posting this information

- posting content (especially photos) that could be reputationally damaging (Ofcom Social Networking qualitative research). Examples range from posting provocative photos to photographs of teachers drinking and smoking being seen by their pupils and pupils' parents

- contacting people they don't know (or don't know well) online, and accepting people they don't know as 'friends' (Ofcom Social Networking qualitative research). Among adult users, 17% say they talk to people that they don't know on social networking sites and 35% speak to people who are 'friends of friends' (Adult Media Literacy Audit 2008).

Our qualitative research indicates that some people are more likely than others to engage in potentially risky behaviour. This suggests that communications about the implications of potentially risky behaviour may need to be looked at in different ways for different groups of people. Our qualitative research also shows that, on the whole, users appear unconcerned about these risks. There are several reasons for this, which include, in no particular order:

- a lack of awareness of the issues

- an assumption that privacy and safety issues have been taken care of by the sites themselves

- low levels of confidence among users in their ability to manipulate privacy settings

- information on privacy and safety being hard to find on sites

- a feeling among younger users that they are invincible

- a perception that social networking sites are less dangerous than other online activities, such as internet banking

- having consciously evaluated the risks, making the decision that they can be managed.

Discussions with children and adults using social networking sites highlight an important point. This is that there is a clear overlap between the benefits and risks of some online social networking activities. For example, the underlying point of social networking is to share information. However, the risk of leaving privacy settings open is that the user cannot control who sees their information or how it is used. Some 44% of adults with current social networking profiles say that their profile is visible to anyone, while 41% of 8–17-year-olds with visible profiles say their profile can be seen by anyone.

The potential risks that we have highlighted raise a number of issues for industry and policymakers. These include how best to enforce the minimum age limits, how to ensure accessible and easy-to-understand privacy and safety policies, ways of educating children, parents and adults about the privacy and safety implications of social networking sites, and the issue of default privacy settings being set to 'open'.

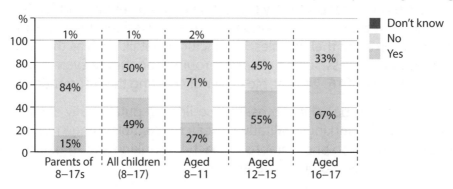

Percentage of parents and children saying they have a profile on a social networking site

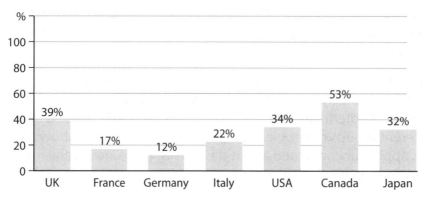

Those with an internet connection who use social networking sites

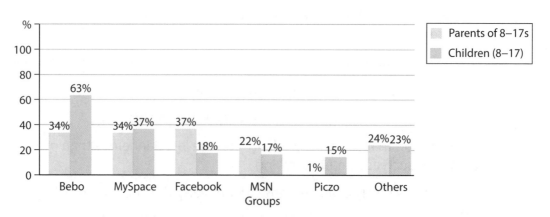

Social networking sites used by parents and children

Research methodologies

Social networking research: qualitative research into attitudes, behaviours and use

Methodology	Qualitative face-to-face survey. This included twelve 2-hour in-depth, paired accompanied surfs; four 90-minute triads; four 90-minute quads; and four 2-hour follow-up online social networking sessions with respondents selected from the triad and quad sessions.
	Respondents who used social networking sites were also asked to complete a pre-task exercise.
Core objective	To identify, explore and understand the behaviours, attitudes and barriers to people's use of social networking sites.
Sample size	52 (39 users and 13 non-users)
Fieldwork period	September–October 2007
Sample definition	Social networking site users and non-users aged 11+. The sample included respondents from each UK nation, and a mix of rural and urban socio-economic groups and genders.

Children, young people and online content research (October 2007)

Methodology	Face-to-face computer-assisted personal interviewing survey (CAPI)
Core objective	To understand the level of current exposure to harmful or inappropriate content and differences in behaviour between parents and children.
Sample size	653 parents, 653 children aged between 5 and 17 from the same households, 279 non-parents
Fieldwork period	October–November 2007
Sample definition	Interviews with parents aged 16–59 and children aged 5–17. The parent and child were recruited from the same household. Only one child was interviewed per household.
	Quotas were set on the age of the child (interviews were split approximately equally between those aged 5–7, 8–11, 12–15 and 16–17), plus gender of parent and gender of child. Scotland, Wales and Northern Ireland were boosted to ensure robust base sizes for analysis.
	Interviews with non-parents aged 16+ who do not live at home with their parents.
	In this instance, non-parents were defined as those without children aged 17 or under living with them.
	Quotas were set on age and gender of the respondent, with Scotland, Wales and Northern Ireland again boosted.
Weighting	Where necessary, the data were weighted to the 2001 census data.

Ofcom media literacy adult audit research

Methodology	Face-to-face, in-home interviews
Core objective	To monitor the extent of media literacy, i.e. the ability of people to access, understand and create communications across key platforms including TV, the internet, mobile phones and radio.
Sample size	2905
Fieldwork period	October–December 2007
Sample definition	UK adults aged 16+
Weighting	Where necessary, the data were weighted to the 2001 census data.

Ofcom communications tracking survey

Methodology	Continuous face-to-face survey
Core objective	To provide Ofcom with continued understanding of consumer behaviour in the UK communications markets to help monitor changes and assess the degree and success of competition.
Sample size	700+ per month (2235 Q3 2007)
Fieldwork period	Q3 2007 (July, August, September)
Sample definition	UK adults aged 15+, reflective of the UK profile by sex, age, socio-economic group, region, employment status, cabled/non-cabled areas, rural/urban areas and levels of deprivation.
Weighting	Where necessary, the data were weighted to ensure they are representative of the UK adult population.

1 Research

Read the task information and identify issues

Guided

1. Begin by reading through the article and identify any areas that you are unclear about. You could do this by highlighting words or phrases and making some initial notes on particular areas. Complete the learner notes below to start analysing the article.

- Page 1 of article: Introduction/executive summary – 'Indicative' means a sign or indication of something ....

....

....

....

- Page 1 of article: Introduction/executive summary – The examples of social networking sites and their function seem out of date. More up-to-date examples are Twitter and

.... which are used to ....

....

....

- ....

....

....

....

....

- ....

....

....

....

Continue to write notes about your initial reactions to the article, looking up unknown words and thinking about potential further areas to research. You may need to use additional pages beyond the space provided here.

When preparing notes, it is useful to start making bullet point notes as soon as possible, however rough, and you can later collate them in a way that works best for you in relation to the focus of the activities.

In this revision Workbook you can refer to any of the notes you have made as you give answers to the activities.

In your actual assessment, you may not be allowed to refer to notes, or there may be restrictions on the length and type of notes that are allowed. You may need to submit your preparatory notes with your answers, so make sure they are legible and clear. Check with your tutor or look at the most up-to-date Sample Assessment Material on the Pearson website for information.

Analyse the task information

> Guided

2. Now thoroughly analyse the article. Here are some questions that will help you to do this. Use bullet points so that your notes are clear and focused.

- When was the research undertaken?

  The research was undertaken between July and December 2007. ....

  ....

  ....

- Is the research source reliable? ....

  ....

  ....

- What qualitative research methods have been used? ....

  ....

  ....

  ....

  ....

- What quantitative research methods have been used? ....

  ....

  ....

  ....

  ....

- Are there any gaps in the research findings? ....

  ....

  ....

  ....

  ....

Links Show that you have thoroughly analysed all sections of the article. See pages 101, 126 and 127 of the Revision Guide for examples of research focus and tips for analysing the stimulus material.

Plan your research

Guided

3. Create a plan of the primary and secondary research that you **could** undertake based on your analysis of the article. It would be useful to relate the primary and secondary research method to a relevant issue you have identified within the article.

My media sector is ....

Issues I have identified are:

1 ....

2 ....

Issue	Primary research	Secondary research
Need research from this year	Hold a focus group with my media peers	Email a questionnaire to college year group

> **Links** Show that you have thoroughly considered the validity and reliability of your sources. See pages 102–105 of the Revision Guide for more information about this, and different research methodologies.

Your research must be related to your own media sector (such as TV, radio, games)

Guided

4. Create a schedule of the primary and secondary research that you **will** undertake. For this revision task, you must not use more than ten sources and you must include a minimum of two primary sources and a minimum of four secondary sources.

You will have a specified amount of time for your research. For your actual assessment, check with your tutor or look at the latest Sample Assessment Material on the Pearson website for details of the number and type of sources you are allowed, and the amount of time you are given to research. Plan your time carefully so you can complete everything you need to in the allocated time.

Primary research	Date	Secondary research	Date	Reliability (secondary research)
1 Hold a focus group with my media peers	10.02.17– 12.02.17	1 Email a questionnaire to college year group	10.02.17	

Undertake your research, make notes and summarise them

6. Undertake your primary and secondary research, recording your results and making notes as you go. Use brief bullet points so that your notes are clear and focused.

> Undertake at least one method of primary, and one method of secondary, research based on the article and notes above so you can practise collating your findings and using them to create your preparatory notes. You may need to use additional pages beyond the space provided here.

....

....

....

....

....

....

....

....

....

....

....

....

....

....

....

....

....

....

....

....

....

....

....

....

....

....

....

Guided

7. Now collate all your notes into a short but clear and informative set of notes to help structure your thinking and prepare to answer the activities. Use bullet points so that your notes are clear and focused. You may wish to include brief quotations, dates and figures. Your notes should relate to both the article and your own research findings.

- The key findings from my primary research were:

....

....

....

....

....

....

....

....

....

....

In this Revision Workbook you can refer to any of the notes you have made as you give answers to the activities.

In your actual assessment, you may not be allowed to refer to notes, or there may be restrictions on the length and type of notes that are allowed. You may need to submit your notes, so make sure they are legible, well organised and easy to understand. Check with your tutor or look at the most up-to-date Sample Assessment Material on the Pearson website for information.

- The key findings from my secondary research were:

....

....

....

....

....

....

....

- My questionnaire results confirmed that ....

....

....

....

....

....

....

 Links See page 131 of the Revision Guide for advice on compiling these notes.

Create a catalogue of sources

 Guided

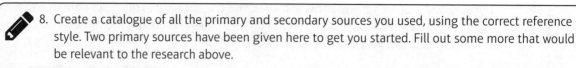

8. Create a catalogue of all the primary and secondary sources you used, using the correct reference style. Two primary sources have been given here to get you started. Fill out some more that would be relevant to the research above.

Primary sources

1 Book: Bryman, A. (2015). *Social Research Methods*. Oxford: Oxford University Press.

2 DVD or film: *The Social Network*. (2010). David Fincher. [DVD] Country: USA.

3 ....

4 ....

5 ....

Secondary sources

6 ....

7 ....

8 ....

9 ....

10 ....

Links Ensure you have correctly referenced all your sources. See pages 114, 116 and 133 of the Revision Guide for guidance on this, and on compiling your catalogue of sources.

Make sure you know the minimum and maximum number of secondary and primary sources you are allowed to use.

You may be required to submit your catalogue as part of your supervised assessment.

Check with your tutor or look at the latest Sample Assessment Material on the Pearson website for more information.

2 Revision activities

To answer the **revision activities** you will have carried out research in relation to the stimulus material on pages 60–66 and made notes.

In the actual assessment:
- The provided piece of stimulus material will be new each year and the research sources will need to relate to it.
- You may not be allowed to use your preparatory notes, or there may be restrictions on the length and type of notes that are allowed. Check with your tutor or look at the latest Sample Assessment Material on the Pearson website for details.

Article: Ofcom 2008: *Social Networking: A quantitative and qualitative research report into attitudes, behaviours and use.*

Guided

1. What are the key issues raised in the article, and how have qualitative and quantitative research been applied to explore them?

The key issues are ....

....

....

....

....

....

....

....

....

....

....

....

....

....

....

....

The article uses quantitative research methods as the findings have been collated from ....

....

....

....

....

....

In relation to the issues, the data highlights that ....

....

....

....

....

....

....

....

....

....

....

The article uses qualitative research methods as the findings have been collated from ....

....

....

....

....

In relation to the issues, the data highlights that ....

....

....

....

....

....

....

....

....

....

....

 Links Show that you have thoroughly considered the question. See page 133 of the Revision Guide for guidance and a worked example. You could use a further piece of paper to continue your answer.

2. How far does the primary and secondary research you have conducted support the conclusions drawn in the article?

The conclusions are ....

....

....

....

....

....

....

My primary research supports the conclusions because ....

....

....

....

However, ...

....

....

My secondary research supports the conclusions because ....

....

....

....

....

....

However, ...

....

....

....

....

Links Show that you have thoroughly considered the question. See page 134 of the Revision Guide for guidance and a worked example. You could use a further piece of paper to continue your answer.

> **Guided**

3. What is the impact of the topic on media production in your specific media sector? Refer to your primary and secondary research in your response.

My media sector is ....

Social media is relevant to this media sector because ....

....

....

....

My questionnaire showed ....

....

....

....

....

My other research suggests ....

....

....

....

....

....

....

Other impacts on the media sector could be ....

....

....

....

....

....

....

Links Show that you have thoroughly considered the question. See page 135 of the Revision Guide for guidance and a worked example. You could use a further piece of paper to continue your answer.

Guided

4. With reference to the article and your own research, how has the topic impacted on consumption patterns in your specific media sector?

Livingstone finds that teenagers present themselves in different ways, based on their ages. Younger participants present 'a highly decorated, stylistically elaborate identity', while older participants aim to create 'a notion of identity lived through authentic relationships with others' (Livingstone, 2008). The creation of these identities, she argues, contains an element of risk which public policy may try to manage ....

....

....

....

....

....

....

....

Examples of the ways social media has impacted my chosen media are ....

....

....

....

....

....

....

....

....

Other impacts on consumption patterns are ....

....

....

....

....

....

Links Show that you have thoroughly considered the question. See page 136 of the Revision Guide for guidance and a worked example. You could use a further piece of paper to continue your answer.

> **Guided**

5. What other research might be carried out in order to gain a greater understanding of the topic? You must refer both to your own research and that carried out in the article.

The article was based on a research study from 2007 and much of it was undertaken one or two years before the article was published. This means the research is at least ten years old. It is important for such a fast-growing subject such as social networking to include more recent findings. Ofcom have some valid reports published in 2015 based on ....

....

....

These are highly relevant statistics as they indicate how ....

....

....

....

....

It would be very beneficial to further research the areas of ....

....

....

using qualitative methods such as ....

....

....

in order to gain a broader perspective of ....

....

....

....

....

....

Links Show that you have thoroughly considered the question. See page 137 of the Revision Guide for guidance. You could use a further piece of paper to continue your answer.

END OF REVISION TASK

Revision task 2

To support your revision, this Workbook contains revision tasks to help you revise the skills that might be needed in your assessed task. The details of the actual assessed task may change so always make sure you are up to date. Ask your tutor or check the Pearson website for the most up-to-date Sample Assessment Material to get an idea of the structure of your assessed task and what this requires of you.

Read the article below. There is space for you to make notes and analyse the article from page 87 onwards.

Task information

Revision Task Information

Stimulus material – article

British Council (2015): *A World of Experience. How international opportunities benefit individuals and employers, and support UK prosperity.*

The following are edited extracts from this report.

British Council overview

The British Council was founded to create 'a friendly knowledge and understanding' between the people of the UK and the wider world. We do this by making a positive contribution to the countries we work with, using the cultural resources of the UK such as art, sport, education, science, culture, language, innovation, creativity and the sharing of the UK's values and ways of living.

A World of Experience (December 2015)

A World of Experience is based on research undertaken by CFE Research and LSE Enterprise on behalf of the British Council, exploring the impact of different types of international experience, including school exchange programmes, volunteering overseas, independent travel, university study and work placements abroad. It provides new insight into how these experiences help to build skills that generate benefits for individuals, employers and UK society in general.

Executive summary

The study highlights three aspects of international experience that are particularly important to the development of skills and which enable individuals to become adept at navigating different cultural contexts and thrive in a global economy:

1. Exposure to cultural difference
2. Duration of exposure
3. Degree of engagement

It also demonstrates that access to a range of activities is vital in reaping the full benefits of international experience, which often accrue over a series of international activities. The survey of UK residents conducted as part of this research found that the vast majority of those with international experience felt it had helped them to develop a number of skills considered important to the contemporary workplace. It also found substantial evidence that involvement in international experience helped to shape participants' career paths. It also identified factors associated with an individual's likelihood to participate in international activities.

Summary of key themes

Skills

Flexibility and adaptability

Over 80% were confident in their ability to adapt to new and unfamiliar situations, crediting their time overseas as a significant factor in acquiring this ability, compared to 70% who did not have international experience.

Innovation skills

○ A large majority of people with international experience described themselves as having abilities needed for innovation, including strong analytical and critical thinking skills (73%) and strong problem-solving skills (83%). Individuals with international experience believed that this had helped them to develop these skills.

○ Seven out of ten were confident communicators, able to work well with people from other countries and cultures.

Languages

While only 26% were confident in their ability to speak a foreign language, they felt their time abroad had helped substantially in achieving this level of confidence. Fewer than one in ten with no international experience felt they were proficient in a foreign language.

Career path

○ Over half of those who had attended university overseas felt the experience had helped them find a job that interested them.

○ Close to half of those who had spent time abroad were involved in innovation within the workplace, including research and development and product improvement activities, compared with around a quarter of those with no international experience.

○ Those with international experience were more likely to be in roles with an international focus, with 60% liaising with international colleagues, suppliers and customers, compared with less than 30% of those without international experience.

Participation

○ The research went on to identify factors associated with an individual's likelihood to participate in overseas international activities. These are:
  ◦ having international experience within the family
  ◦ speaking a foreign language
  ◦ having a degree.

○ While more research is needed to confirm this, it is likely that many individuals who do not have this profile may be missing out on opportunities for personal development. Given the additional benefits gained by individuals participating in international activities, this poses important questions regarding equity and social mobility.

- There was significant variance between males and females at each end of the spectrum of international opportunities, with girls more likely to take part in school exchanges, and men more likely to take up opportunities to work abroad. The proportion undertaking university-level study abroad was similar for both genders. Men were more likely to have experiences of three months or more, or multiple international experiences.

Provision of international opportunities

School-level activities

International education initiatives in primary schools typically focus on building links with schools overseas rather than travelling abroad. A recent report by the Institute of Education suggests that:

- 82% of primary schools have links with schools abroad
- 62% encourage pupils to correspond with students in overseas schools.

International trips and school exchanges are also becoming less common due to pressures on school resources, worries about health and safety, and child protection. A recently commissioned survey revealed that:

- only 39% of British secondary schools now run traditional exchange trips involving a stay with a host family
- of these, only 30% of state schools reported that they run such exchanges, whereas 77% of independent schools said they did
- in addition, recent changes in the National Curriculum have reduced incentives for schools to incorporate a global dimension into lessons.

Tertiary education

UNESCO Institute for Statistics (the latest internationally comparable statistics) estimates as follows.

- Twenty-eight thousand UK students were undertaking their whole degree in another country in 2012 – a figure that has been relatively consistent since 1999 and represents around 1% of the population in higher education.
- In contrast, the number of students coming to the UK from abroad is significantly higher and grew year-on-year to 2012.
- The US is the most popular destination for UK students undertaking their entire course abroad, with around 9000 individuals on courses in the country.
- According to the latest globally comparable student mobility figures, the UK is the second most popular international study destination for students undertaking their entire degree abroad, hosting 13% of internationally mobile students in 2012.

Gap years

A gap year can take many forms and be in different places. It is usually understood to mean a break in full-time education between sitting A levels and starting university, often devoted to travel and/or work. For the purposes of this study, it has been defined as a period between three and 24 months.

Measuring participation is challenging and there is a lack of up-to-date data on the number of individuals in the UK taking a gap year.

○ In 2003, the figure was around 50 000 per year, but this figure may have changed significantly since then.

○ Some 60% of those who had actively planned a gap year travelled abroad at some point during the period, while 15% worked abroad and approximately another 15% volunteered abroad.

Working abroad

UK citizens are more likely to report that they have lived and worked abroad than their European counterparts.

○ Some 16% of UK respondents to a Eurobarometer study indicated that they had lived and worked in another country, compared with the European average of 10% and 8% for Germany.

○ It showed that UK respondents were also more likely to have family and friends who had worked abroad – 48% versus 29%.

○ There are formal programmes offering work placements abroad. However, the extent of participation in these schemes is difficult to assess, as information is both dispersed and proprietary.

Key findings

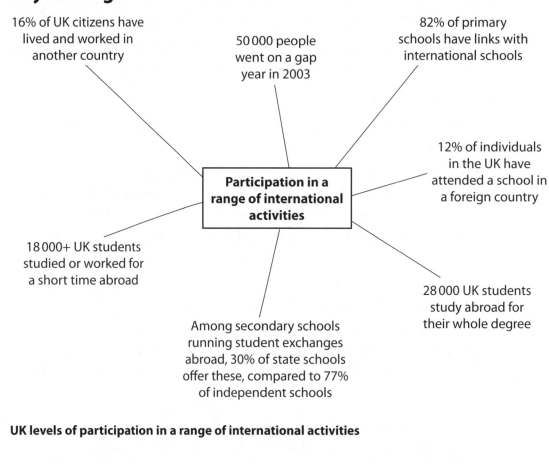

16% of UK citizens have lived and worked in another country

50 000 people went on a gap year in 2003

82% of primary schools have links with international schools

12% of individuals in the UK have attended a school in a foreign country

Participation in a range of international activities

18 000+ UK students studied or worked for a short time abroad

Among secondary schools running student exchanges abroad, 30% of state schools offer these, compared to 77% of independent schools

28 000 UK students study abroad for their whole degree

UK levels of participation in a range of international activities

		Strongly agree		Agree	

Increased confidence

	Strongly agree	Agree
Travel	47%	47%
Study	37%	49%
Work experience	46%	47%

Increased curiosity

	Strongly agree	Agree
Travel	37%	50%
Study	33%	48%
Work experience	33%	45%

Increased tolerance

	Strongly agree	Agree
Travel	33%	48%
Study	27%	50%
Work experience	31%	50%

Impact of international experience on confidence, curiosity and tolerance

Source: CFE Research (2014). Base: 25–65-year-olds in UK (1148 total; 712 with international experience)

Life and career skills

The research found that the vast majority of those with international experience believed that it had enabled them to develop as a person. It also indicated that experience gained later in life may offer greater opportunity for personal development compared with experiences at a younger age.

Some 84% of survey respondents who had worked abroad or travelled extensively believed that they had developed as a person during their time overseas, compared with 74% of those who had attended university in another country and with 67% of those with school-level experiences.

'I think it makes you kind of aware of keeping an open mind about things, and about issues, and trying to work out what's really going on as opposed to what you're told.' *Dancer, studied abroad for 12 months*

Learning and innovation skills

○ Respondents with international experience were more likely to report that they had:

  ○ strong analytical and critical thinking skills (73%; 13 percentage points higher than those without such experience)

  ○ problem-solving skills (83%; +11 percentage points)

  ○ a creative mindset (66%; +9 percentage points)

○ Some 70% of those who had worked abroad believed their international experience was a significant factor in helping them to develop a creative mindset.

○ Some 68% of those who worked abroad also attributed the development of strong problem-solving abilities to their international experience.

Career path

One argument that is well rehearsed in support of international experience is that it enables participants to demonstrate exposure to 'real-life problems', pick up valuable skills and ensure their CV stands out when it comes to applying for a job. Some of the interviews conducted for this study supported these views:

'I think it was really good on my CV for future job interviews, showing that I had travelled for a year and was able to do the logistics of arranging that.' *Healthcare professional, worked abroad for one year and travelled abroad for 13 months*

The survey found that:

○ 53% reported that it helped them to get a job that interested them

○ 47% indicated it enabled them to secure a job of any kind

○ 42% felt the experience had helped them to decide on their ideal career path

○ 38% reported it also helped them to open up immediate or short-term job opportunities in their chosen career path

○ 38% indicated they progressed more quickly towards their long-term career aspirations.

Personal engagement

The survey findings indicate that there is an association between international experience and higher levels of engagement. This is one of the key ingredients in developing intercultural skills. Through navigating an unfamiliar environment, individuals begin to appreciate their ability to overcome hurdles and make an active contribution which provides the motivation and empowerment needed to face future obstacles. In many cases, particularly where individuals have been involved in volunteering overseas, this also translates as a greater global and local civic awareness, as an individual's outlook on international affairs and appreciation of their ability to bring benefits to others is influenced by their international experience. One interviewee with experience of working abroad stated that they came back:

'with such a strong resolve to try and address systemic issues around why people were living in poverty or development or why the market had failed them.' *Consultant, volunteered abroad for six months*

Research methodology

To explore the impact of international experiences undertaken by UK citizens, the British Council commissioned CFE Research and LSE Enterprise to review existing evidence and undertake new research to explore the specific benefits arising for individuals, the economy and wider society from different types and lengths of international experience. This consisted of:

○ a literature review on the UK's competitiveness and skills needs

○ a literature review on opportunities for international experience in the UK, and a comparison with the US and Germany

○ a survey of 1148 UK residents between the ages of 25 and 65, of whom 712 had international experiences and 436 had no international experience

○ semi-structured interviews with individuals who have had international experiences

○ case studies of a range of programmes that enable people to develop international experience.

Profile of participants

It is important to consider the profile of those most likely to participate in and benefit from the opportunities available. The research sought to understand more about the group with no international experience, particularly why they had decided not to participate in international activities. A large majority (75%) of respondents without international experience confirmed they were aware such opportunities exist. However, further analysis suggests that some groups may be better informed about the opportunities than others. A greater proportion of individuals with a degree (83%) were aware of such opportunities compared with those respondents without a degree (72%). Awareness also increased with socio-economic status. It was 85% among the most privileged group but was still high, at 71%, among the less privileged. There were also significant differences by gender, with a significantly higher proportion of male respondents (85%) aware of international opportunities compared with female respondents (71%).

However, caution should be taken with the results from this analysis, as it is difficult to determine the direction of the relationship in all instances. Further research is needed to determine why and how these factors appear to influence levels of participation.

Conclusions

The research found that a wide variety of programmes are available to young people at different stages of education offering the opportunity to travel, volunteer and work abroad. There is, however, a lack of public and consistent data available which means it is challenging to gain a comprehensive overview of the scale, nature and impact of these opportunities, while meaningful comparison between the UK and other countries is virtually impossible. The limited data available at higher education level suggest that, while UK students may be more likely to pursue international opportunities than their US counterparts, take-up of these opportunities is not at the level seen in some other countries.

Limited understanding of the impact of international experiences on the individual and the associated benefits may be one aspect affecting demand. Young people may be opting not to work or study abroad because it is unclear whether it will affect their future employability. Among employers, there is an appreciation that working and studying abroad can support skills development, but there is little evidence that they are looking for individuals with international experience when recruiting – something which would be likely to drive take-up among young people.

To promote the benefits of international experiences more effectively, those offering such opportunities need to better understand what makes a more powerful experience and actively promote the development of appropriate opportunities.

Finally, the research indicated that there appear to be differing levels of participation in international experiences by different social groups, which, considering the benefits that can be derived from these experiences, poses important challenges for equity and social mobility.

Given the clear benefits that derive from international experience for individuals, employers and the UK economy, it is important that more young people are given the opportunity to participate in these experiences in the future. This research suggests that increasing and widening access to these opportunities could make an important contribution to future UK prosperity.

Recommendations

- Recognise and promote the benefits of international experience.
- Encourage participation from an early age.
- Widen access to international opportunities.
- Reinforce the connections between international experience and innovation.
- Identify and build on benefits.
- Reinforce foreign language benefits.
- Deepen understanding of the benefits.
- Benchmark participation.
- Seek to understand the barriers to participation.

1 Research

Read the task information and identify issues

> Begin by reading through the revision task information (the article) and identify and make notes about any areas that you are unclear about, and any initial ideas about what you might want to research further. Use bullet points so that your notes are clear and focused.

....

....

....

....

....

....

....

....

....

....

....

....

....

....

....

....

....

....

....

....

....

....

....

....

....

Analyse the task information, and plan and undertake your research

Now analyse the revision task information more thoroughly. Start to define the key issues that you think will require further research. Plan and start carrying out this research and make notes about it, including source references using the correct style. Use additional paper if you need to. Use bullet points so that your notes are clear and focused. You may wish to include brief quotations, dates and figures.

....
....
....
....
....
....
....
....
....
....
....
....
....
....
....
....
....
....
....
....
....
....
....
....
....
....
....

Summarise your notes and findings

Collate notes which summarise your findings about the article and your own additional research, to help structure your thinking and prepare to answer the activities. Use bullet points so that your notes are clear and focused. You may wish to include brief quotations, dates and figures.

In this Revision Workbook you can refer to any of the notes you have made as you give answers to the activities.

In your actual assessment, you may not be allowed to refer to notes, or there may be restrictions on the length and type of notes that are allowed. You may need to submit your notes, so make sure they are legible, well organised and easy to understand. Check with your tutor or look at the most up-to-date Sample Assessment Material on the Pearson website for information.

Continue your notes on this page. Make sure your notes include specific data from your secondary research.

....
....
....
....
....
....
....
....
....
....
....
....
....
....
....
....
....
....
....
....
....
....
....
....
....
....
....
....
....
....

Continue your summary of your notes and findings on this page.

Continue your summary of your notes and findings on this page.

Provide a fully referenced catalogue of the primary and secondary sources you have used in your research in addition to the stimulus material (for this revision task, no more than ten sources).

Primary sources

....

....

....

....

....

....

....

....

....

....

Secondary sources

....

....

....

....

....

....

....

....

....

....

....

Make sure you know the minimum and maximum number of secondary and primary sources you are allowed to use.

You may be required to submit your catalogue as part of your supervised assessment.

Check with your tutor or look at the latest Sample Assessment Material on the Pearson website for more information.

2 Revision activities

Use the notes you have made on the previous five pages to answer the questions below.

In the actual assessment:

- The provided piece of stimulus material will be new each year and the research sources will need to relate to it.
- You may not be allowed to use your preparatory notes, or there may be restrictions on the length and type of notes that are allowed. Check with your tutor or look at the latest Sample Assessment Material on the Pearson website for details.

Article: British Council 2015: *A World of Experience: How international opportunities benefit individuals and employers, and support UK prosperity*

1. What are the key issues raised in the article, and how have qualitative and quantitative research been applied to explore them?

....

....

....

....

....

....

....

....

....

....

....

....

....

....

....

....

....

....

....

....

You could use a further piece of paper to continue your answer.

2. How far do the primary and secondary research you have conducted support the conclusions drawn in the article?

....

....

....

....

....

....

....

....

....

....

....

....

....

....

....

....

....

....

....

....

....

....

....

....

....

....

....

....

....

....

....

| You could use a further piece of paper to continue your answer. |

3. What is the impact of the topic on media production in your specific media sector? Refer to your primary and secondary research in your response.

....

....

....

....

....

....

....

....

....

....

....

....

....

....

....

....

....

....

....

....

....

....

....

....

....

....

....

....

....

....

....

You could use a further piece of paper to continue your answer.

4. With reference to the article and your own research, how has the topic impacted on consumption patterns in your specific media sector?

....

....

....

....

....

....

....

....

....

....

....

....

....

....

....

....

....

....

....

....

....

....

....

....

....

....

....

....

....

....

You could use a further piece of paper to continue your answer.

5. What other research might be carried out in order to gain a greater understanding of the topic? You must refer both to your own research and that carried out in the article.

....

....

....

....

....

....

....

....

....

....

....

....

....

....

....

....

....

....

....

....

....

....

....

....

....

....

....

You could use a further piece of paper to continue your answer.

END OF REVISION TASK

Unit 8: Responding to a Commission

Your set task

Unit 8 will be assessed through a task, which will be set by Pearson. You will need to use your understanding of the commissioning process and how to respond to client briefs by generating ideas using a range of skills.

Your Revision Workbook

This Workbook is designed to **revise skills** that might be needed in your assessed task. The selected content, outcomes, questions and answers are provided to help you to revise content and ways of applying your skills. Ask your tutor or check the **Pearson website** for the most up-to-date **Sample Assessment Material** to get an indication of the structure of your assessed task and what this requires of you. The details of the actual assessed task may change so always make sure you are up to date.

To support your revision, this Workbook contains revision tasks to help you revise the skills that might be needed in your assessed task. Each revision task is divided into two sections.

1 Formulating ideas in response to a commission

In this section you will use your skills to:
- read and analyse a brief and information from a client (pages 100–103)
- choose the commission you wish to respond to (pages 104–105)
- generate and plan ideas in response to the brief and your chosen commission (pages 106–109).

2 Responding to a commission

In this section you will practise writing:
- a rationale (pages 110–112)
- a pitch (pages 113–114)
- a proposal (pages 115–122)
- a treatment (pages 123–125).

Links To help you revise skills that might be needed in your Unit 8 set task this Workbook contains two revision tasks, starting on pages 100 and 126. The first is guided and models good techniques, to help you develop your skills. The second gives you the opportunity to apply the skills you have developed. See the Introduction on page iii for more information on features included to help you revise.

Revision task 1

To support your revision, this Workbook contains two revision tasks to help you revise the skills that might be needed in your assessed task. The details of the actual assessed task may change so always make sure you are up to date. Ask your tutor or check the Pearson website for the most up-to-date Sample Assessment Material to get an idea of the structure of your assessed task and what this requires of you.

1 Formulating ideas in response to a commission

1. Read the revision task information that follows carefully.

2. Analyse the information provided. Use the activities provided to help you to do this.

3. Choose **one** commission only for your response:
   - Commission 1 – Promotional video
   - Commission 2 – Website
   - Commission 3 – Radio advertisement
   - Commission 4 – Poster campaign
   - Commission 5 – Digital game

4. Generate and plan ideas in response to your chosen commission and medium using the information provided. You will need to plan material to allow you to create:
   - Your rationale
   - Your pitch
   - Your proposal
   - Your treatment

Task information

Start by reading the task information. Remember that this is example task information only, and the organisation described is not real.

healthylifeuk.com

HealthyLifeUK is an organisation aiming to promote health and fitness among the UK population.

> **Press release from HealthyLifeUK**
>
> HealthyLifeUK is an independent organisation set up to promote healthy lifestyles to people across the UK.
>
> Over a quarter of all deaths in the UK are caused by cardiovascular diseases – that is, diseases of the heart and circulation, including heart failure, coronary heart disease and strokes. Key risk factors for these diseases are poor diet, inactivity, high blood pressure levels and consumption of addictive substances like tobacco and alcohol.
>
> Trends indicate that unhealthy lifestyle choices are having an impact on young people and that the risk factors known to cause heart problems are widespread. HealthyLifeUK is centring on how a lack of physical activity can contribute to those risk factors and ultimately lead to serious illness. The core focus is on people aged 25–40.
>
> HealthyLifeUK believes the only way to combat this major risk to the health and well-being of the population is through education and guidance on the risk factors of unhealthy lifestyle choices, and through positive and proactive advice and encouragement to make healthy choices. In our current campaign, we want to provide clear, supportive guidance on the impact that unhealthy lifestyle choices can have on an individual, as well as alerting younger people to the possible long-term damage caused by choices earlier in life. Our aim is to be informative and supportive rather than dictating demands or being judgemental. Those who we want to reach should see us as a helping hand when making decisions about their lifestyles for their own gain.
>
> HealthyLifeUK is an independent and impartial organisation. We receive some government funding but we also rely on funding from charitable organisations and businesses.

Analyse the information provided. In your **rationale** you will need to explain what you intend to produce, with justifications for how your product meets the requirements of the commission.

Guided

To help you generate ideas for your rationale, you need to gather key information about the client from this press release. Here are some questions that will help you make brief notes to do this.

1. What are the main aims of HealthyLifeUK?

To promote healthy lifestyles across the UK. ....

....

....

....

Guided

2. What does HealthyLifeUK hope to communicate to its audience?

That lack of physical fitness can cause heart problems. ....

....

....

....

....

3. What specifically has HealthyLifeUK stated about the way it wants to communicate this information?

....

....

....

....

4. How is HealthyLifeUK funded?

....

....

....

5. Who is HealthyLifeUK hoping to reach with its campaigns?

....

....

....

....

....

Links You can revise the skills needed for analysing task information on page 168 of the Revision Guide.

It is useful to consider how competitors have dealt with issues similar to those in the task information. For example, you could do some internet research, using search terms such as 'healthy lifestyle companies' and 'health and wellness charities'.

Guided

6. How have other organisations that have worked on similar remits tackled the challenge, and how can this inform your rationale?

One other organisation I identified was ....

Their approach to this issue is ....

....

....

....

....

You will need to justify your suggestions in the rationale by including facts and figures. Read the supporting data provided by HealthyLifeUK.

Supporting data

Cardiovascular disease

Every 3 minutes …

someone dies from cardiovascular disease in the UK.

42 000 people under 75 …

die from cardiovascular disease each year.

High blood pressure

Nearly 30% of all adults in the UK have high blood pressure.

Blood cholesterol levels

52% of all adults in the UK have elevated blood cholesterol levels.

Lifestyle risk factors (UK)	
Smoking	One in six adults smokes.
Body weight	Over a third of all adults are classed as overweight.
Exercise	Nearly two out of five adults do not achieve recommended levels of physical activity.
Poor diet	Only a quarter of adults consume the recommended five portions of fruit or vegetables a day.

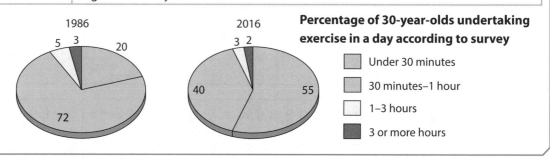

1986

5 3 20

72

2016

3 2

40 55

Percentage of 30-year-olds undertaking exercise in a day according to survey

- Under 30 minutes
- 30 minutes–1 hour
- 1–3 hours
- 3 or more hours

✏️ Read the charts and tables. Make brief notes that identify the key facts being communicated.

1. What percentage of adults in the UK has high blood pressure?

....

....

2. How many people under 75 die from cardiovascular disease each year?

....

....

3. What percentage of 30-year-olds surveyed in 2016 do between 30 minutes and 1 hour of exercise a day?

....

....

4. What percentage difference is that compared to 30-year-olds in 1986?

....

....

⟩ Guided ⟩

5. Which key facts or figures do you think would be most useful in convincing your target audience of the importance of the message HealthyLifeUK wants to convey? List them here as bullet points.

• Every 3 minutes someone in the UK dies from cardiovascular disease. ....

....

....

....

....

....

....

....

....

You could make brief notes as you go along and keep track of where any ideas came from and why you made certain decisions, to help you plan your rationale.

In this Workbook you can refer to any of the notes you have made as you give answers to the activities.

In your actual assessment, you may not be allowed to refer to notes, or there may be restrictions on the length and type of notes that are allowed. Check with your tutor or look at the most up-to-date Sample Assessment Material on the Pearson website for information.

Now choose a revision commission that you would undertake, taking into account your own subject specialisms, skills and understanding.

REVISION COMMISSION 1: INFORMATIONAL VIDEO

HealthyLifeUK needs a short (five minutes, maximum) informational video for use on our website and social media platforms. The video will promote our current campaign to raise awareness of risk factors for cardiovascular disease and to encourage healthy lifestyle choices. The target audience is people aged 25–40.

We expect this resource to be ready by mid-December so it can be launched to coincide with our 'New You' campaign in the new year. Therefore, you will need to demonstrate that you have carefully considered the timescales and potential logistics of tackling this project.

We have sent this request to a number of different creative media production companies, so you will need to persuade us to take your idea forward in this competitive field.

We look forward to hearing from you.

REVISION COMMISSION 2: INTERACTIVE WEBSITE

HealthyLifeUK needs a website (at least four pages of content) to promote our current campaign to raise awareness of risk factors for cardiovascular disease and to encourage healthy lifestyle choices. The target audience is people aged 25–40.

We expect this resource to be ready by mid-December so it can be launched to coincide with our 'New You' campaign in the new year. Therefore, you will need to demonstrate that you have carefully considered the timescales and potential logistics of tackling this project.

We have sent this request to a number of different creative media production companies, so you will need to persuade us to take your idea forward in this competitive field.

We look forward to hearing from you.

REVISION COMMISSION 3: RADIO ADVERTISEMENT

HealthyLifeUK needs a 90-second radio advert to promote our current campaign to raise awareness of risk factors for cardiovascular disease and to encourage healthy lifestyle choices. The target audience is people aged 25–40.

We expect this resource to be ready by mid-December so it can be launched to coincide with our 'New You' campaign in the new year. Therefore, you will need to demonstrate that you have carefully considered the timescales and potential logistics of tackling this project.

We have sent this request to a number of different creative media production companies, so you will need to persuade us to take your idea forward in this competitive field.

We look forward to hearing from you.

REVISION COMMISSION 4: POSTER CAMPAIGN

HealthyLifeUK needs at least four different posters to promote our current campaign to raise awareness of risk factors for cardiovascular disease and to encourage healthy lifestyle choices. The target audience is people aged 25–40.

We expect this resource to be ready by mid-December so it can be launched to coincide with our 'New You' campaign in the new year. Therefore, you will need to demonstrate that you have carefully considered the timescales and potential logistics of tackling this project.

We have sent this request to a number of different creative media production companies, so you will need to persuade us to take your idea forward in this competitive field.

We look forward to hearing from you.

REVISION COMMISSION 5: SMARTPHONE PUZZLE GAME

HealthyLifeUK needs a digital puzzle game with at least three levels that is suitable for smartphone use. The game will promote our current campaign to raise awareness of risk factors for cardiovascular disease and to encourage healthy lifestyle choices. The target audience is people aged 25–40.

We expect this resource to be ready by mid-December so it can be launched to coincide with our 'New You' campaign in the new year. Therefore, you will need to demonstrate that you have carefully considered the timescales and potential logistics of tackling this project.

We have sent this request to a number of different creative media production companies, so you will need to persuade us to take your idea forward in this competitive field.

We look forward to hearing from you.

Plan ideas for your **pitch**. You will need to persuade the client of the value of your proposal. Making clear and succinct notes about your planned content will help you.

When you have chosen the commission to undertake, make brief notes that identify the key features of that commission below.

1. What medium have you chosen to work in (for example, moving image, print-based) and why?

   ....

2. What length/duration/extent has the client specified you must provide?

   ....

   ....

3. What messages has the client asked you to communicate within the product?

   ....

   ....

   ....

   ....

   ....

4. When does the finished product need to be ready by?

   ....

   ....

5. List key features of your product, with a short explanation about how they meet the brief.

   ,...

   ....

   ....

   ....

   ....

6. How will your product stand out against similar products already in the market? What will be its unique selling point (USP)?

   ....

   ....

   ....

   ....

   ....

Links See page 171 of the Revision Guide for advice on making notes.

7. Look at these suggestions for persuasive, positive words. Choose **three** examples and write a sentence about your proposed idea for each word you have chosen.

creative   innovative   (engaging)   unique   popular   successful   appealing   imaginative

This engaging concept will attract your target audience because ....

....

....

....

....

Plan ideas for your **proposal**, where you will need to expand on your idea and provide more detail about the intended audience experience and practical production of your product.

Consider the content of your product and provide a bit more detail using brief notes to help you write a content overview.

1. What presentation style are you using (e.g. is it serious or fun)?

....

....

2. Give **one** specific example of content that you will include in your product.

....

....

3. Identify any particular colours, images or themes that will be featured.

....

....

4. What will your audience experience when using the product?

> Think about your target audience's journey when using the product, from beginning to end. Depending on the medium, this could be the stages of a story, intended order of click-throughs, levels of a game, or a page plan.

....

....

....

....

....

....

5. What do you intend your audience to do after they have finished their 'journey'? This is known as the 'call to action'.

....

....

....

6. You will also need to include the practicalities of producing your intended product in your proposal.

   Use the table to summarise the technical considerations you need to take into account, including personnel, locations, any assets and equipment.

> Personnel means particular people who need to contribute or carry out work in order to complete your planned product.

Equipment	Reason for use	Personnel required	Location or assets required	Possible issues	Possible solutions
Video camera	To film professional quality footage of latest HealthyLifeUK campaign in a school, to include on website	Camera operator who owns tripod and has experience using it	Need to sort suitable date with school	Need to get permission to include students in footage if under 18	Ask school to make parents aware of our filming day

7. What legal and ethical considerations do you need to take into account?

> For example, you will need to take care in what you say about any specific tobacco or alcohol companies to avoid legal implications. Similarly, ensure all your information and advice around the treatment of people at high risk of cardiovascular disease is ethical in nature.

....

....

....

....

....

....

....

8. When is the deadline for your finished product?

....

....

9. What stages, in order from first to last, do you need to go through to get to your finished product?

Don't forget to incorporate opportunities for the client to feed back.

....

....

....

....

....

The final part of your commission response should provide a **treatment** for your intended product.
A treatment should provide a short sample of what your idea will look like or sound like.

 Think about the order in which your content is going to appear and use the space below to map it out, using minimal sketches where appropriate.

Consider any sketches, script summaries, plot summaries, page plans, site maps, etc. to help you complete your treatment.

In this Workbook you can refer to any of the notes you have made as you respond to the commission.

In your actual assessment, you may not be allowed to refer to notes, or there may be restrictions on the length and type of notes that are allowed. Check with your tutor or look at the most up-to-date Sample Assessment Material on the Pearson website for information.

2. Responding to a commission

To respond to the commission, you will have read and analysed a brief and commission from a client, chosen a commission to respond to, planned ideas, and prepared for writing a commission response.

In the actual assessment:
- The brief and commissions will be new each year.
- You may not be allowed to use your preparatory notes, or there may be restrictions on the length and type of preparatory notes that are allowed. Check with your tutor or look at the latest Sample Assessment Material on the Pearson website for details.
- Some templates may be provided for your treatment, or you can use your own appropriate templates.

You must complete ALL sections.

You will need to refer to the task information on pages 104–105 and any preparatory notes you have made. You must complete all the tasks for your chosen commission in a limited time, so plan your time carefully.

You will have a limited time in which to complete your commission response in the supervised assessment. Plan your time carefully to ensure you complete everything you need to within the allocated time. Ask your tutor or look at the Sample Assessment Material on the Pearson website for details.

Rationale

If you are asked to write a rationale, always check if there is a word limit.

To check the word limit in your supervised assessment, ask your tutor or check the most up-to-date Sample Assessment Material on the Pearson website.

Links You can revise the skills needed for writing a rationale for moving image or print-based products on pages 172 and 173 of the Revision Guide. For more general advice, see page 150 of the Revision Guide.

 HealthyLifeUK is looking for ideas that will meet its commission and demonstrate that the data provided has been used to generate appropriate concepts.

You have been asked to write a rationale explaining your ideas in response to the commission you have chosen. HealthyLifeUK will need to know how you used the information provided to form your ideas (maximum 500 words).

First of all, explain what key information you noted from the brief and how this helped to guide your initial investigations.

My initial investigations were guided by the following key information that I noted from the brief:

....

....

....

....

....

....

....

Explain in detail how you have used the content from the brief in developing your work, referring to specific examples from the information you were provided.

I used the content of the brief to develop my work further by ....

....

....

....

....

....

....

Explain in detail how the ideas you have proposed meet the specific nature of the commission you were given.

My proposed ideas are suitable for this commission because ....

....

....

....

....

....

....

....

How would you justify, with specific examples from your own research and investigation, why you have made your suggestions?

My own research and investigation supports these suggestions in the following ways:

....

....

....

....

....

....

....

....

....

....

....

....

....

....

....

....

Give examples of existing work and also state what you have learned from them.

Examples of similar existing work which have inspired or informed my work are ....

....

....

....

....

....

....

....

....

....

....

....

....

....

....

....

....

....

....

Pitch

HealthyLifeUK has sent this commission to a number of different production companies. You will therefore need to convey your idea in a succinct and persuasive way through a written pitch. You will need to 'sell' the idea to the client by including an overview of the content and style of your solution to the brief to persuade them that it is worth considering.

> **Guided**

Write a pitch to promote your idea to HealthyLifeUK in a maximum of 350 words.

> If you are asked to write a pitch, always check if there is a word limit.
>
> To check the word limit in your supervised assessment, ask your tutor or check the most up-to-date Sample Assessment Material on the Pearson website.

> **Links** You can revise the skills needed for writing a pitch for moving image or print-based products on page 174 of the Revision Guide. For more general advice see pages 151 and 152 of the Revision Guide.

> Begin by stating which commission you chose to take forward and why you chose this one. Use positive and persuasive words. This should be one short sentence.

The commission I chose was ....

The reason I chose this commission was ....

....

....

> Explain why you find this an engaging or interesting commission to respond to. Remember to maintain your persuasive tone by being positive and enthusiastic.

....

....

....

....

....

....

> Give a two-sentence overview of the nature of the product you have generated ideas for.

....

....

....

....

....

....

....

Explain how this idea meets the brief, and why. Give examples of how it would appeal to the target audience, communicate the intended message and promote the client's cause.

This would appeal to the target audience because ....

....

....

....

....

....

....

This would communicate your intended messages about the importance of a healthy lifestyle by ....

....

....

....

....

This will raise awareness of these issues in your target audience by ....

....

....

....

....

Explain in detail a particular element or detail of the product that you feel makes your idea unique and stronger than competing products.

....

....

....

....

....

Proposal

The proposal documents you present here are intended to expand on the idea you have generated and summarised in the pitch and should provide further detail about your proposed project. The proposal requires details of:

- content overview
- technical considerations
- contributors, assets, locations and equipment
- legal and ethical considerations
- scheduling and planning considerations.

Complete the boxes at the top of each of the five sections, identifying your proposal.

Proposal (medium)	Producer (name)	Title of production	Page number

Links You can revise the skills needed for writing a content overview for moving image or print-based products on page 175 of the Revision Guide. For more general advice on writing a proposal see pages 154–157 of the Revision Guide.

> **Guided**

Content overview

> Begin by defining the overall style or nature of your product. What will the intended mood of this piece be? Is it going to be upbeat and bright or more reflective?

The overall mood of my product will be ....

....

....

....

> What themes will you include in the piece and how will you do this? For example, a medical or clinical theme might use a lot of red and white, and depending on the medium, feature images of medical equipment.

I will address the theme of ....

One technique I will use to do this is ....

....

....

....

....

....

....

> What existing media products will it be similar to in style?

....

....

....

Now give an overview of how the product will be experienced by the viewer. For moving image, audio and games products this might be a description of the narrative or action. For web-based products and print-based media this might be a description of how you will guide the reader through the content provided.

....

....

....

....

....

....

....

....

....

....

You should detail how the intended product will end (depending on the medium). Explain how this ending will allow users to explore the subject further – for example, via links or other calls to action – and how you will give it a professional ending suitable to the medium.

The final part of my product will ....

....

....

....

....

....

....

....

This will generate a call to action by ....

....

....

....

....

....

....

....

Proposal (medium)	Producer (name)	Title of production	Page number

> Guided

Technical considerations

Give details of the equipment you intend to use to produce your proposed product.

I intend to use ....

....

....

Explain why would you use this particular equipment to produce this product.

The reason I am using this equipment is ....

....

....

Explain if any of this equipment is hard to get hold of or if it has any special requirements/requires specialist personnel to operate/needs additional considerations.

....

....

....

Describe any specific plans you have for your product that might create difficult technical challenges. For example, you could consider lighting on location for a moving image product, content-rich websites, difficult-to-source imagery in a print product, and so on.

....

....

....

Explain how you intend to overcome these particular challenges. Consider the equipment, personnel, time considerations or skills you may require in order to solve these issues.

To overcome any challenges I intend to ....

....

....

....

....

Proposal (medium)	Producer (name)	Title of production	Page number

> **Guided**

Contributors, assets, locations and equipment

> List the contributors you intend to use in your product. This could include onscreen talent, voice actors, interviewees, models for photographs, or presenters.

The contributors I intend to use are ....

....

....

> What skills will people require for these roles? How will your choice of contributors connect with, appeal to or relate to the target audience?

My contributors will need to be able to ....

....

....

....

> List the locations you will need to film in, photograph or use in order to produce this product.

....

....

....

> Do these locations present any particular logistical or technical challenges? Consider how you would get cast, models and crew there; whether you would need to gain permission from the owner of the location; whether you would need additional light; and what the safety concerns are about working in the environment.

Possible challenges include ....

....

....

....

....

> Detail any props, costumes, bought-in content, stock photography, music tracks, make-up or other additional assets you could not generate by yourself.

Items/assets that I need, which I am unable to generate myself, include ....

....

....

Why do you need these and how will they enhance or improve the product you are intending to make?

I need these items/assets because ....

....

....

....

You've already outlined the technical equipment you hope to use in the technical considerations section. Here, you can outline any further equipment you may need to hire and facilities you might need to access, such as edit suites, web-design software, industry-standard hardware and computers.

....

....

....

....

....

....

....

Proposal (medium)	Producer (name)	Title of production	Page number

Legal and ethical considerations

> Consider whether all the content you intend to include will be generated completely by you. If not, what may be from elsewhere?

The content that I intend to use from elsewhere includes ....

....

....

....

> Is there anything that could infringe copyright law, such as music created by someone else, images made by someone else, or slogans or logos of companies? If so, how will you avoid or solve this issue?

To avoid any copyright issues I am going to ....

....

....

....

> Think carefully about the proposed content of your piece. Is there anything that could be controversial, offensive or challenging to particular groups in society?

....

....

....

....

....

....

....

> If so, how will you ensure you deal with this in a sensitive way in order to meet the requirements of equality law?

....

....

....

....

How will you ensure that health and safety laws are not infringed while you are working on this project? What precautions and processes will you put in place to ensure you, your team and others involved or nearby are not exposed to risks?

To ensure that health and safety laws are not infringed, I intend to ....

....

....

....

....

....

....

....

....

What regulatory body codes may need to be considered when working on a product like this and how will you ensure you meet their codes?

The regulatory codes I may need to consider include ....

....

....

....

....

....

Proposal (medium)	Producer (name)	Title of production	Page number

Scheduling and planning considerations

> When is your deadline for this project and why is this important?

The deadline for the project is ....

This is important because ....

....

> How do you intend to plan and manage your time and that of the production team throughout the project? Consider what documents or processes you might use for this.

I will plan and manage my own and the production teams' time by ....

....

....

....

....

....

> What will you need to tackle first in the project and why?

The first thing I need to tackle on the project is ....

....

....

> How will you build in opportunities for the client to feed back or review your progress within this schedule?

Client feedback and progress reviews will be built in through ....

....

....

....

Treatment

A treatment would include samples of how your final idea will look, sound and/or feel.

HealthyLifeUK has asked you to produce development documentation to help convey what the finished product will be like. Use the relevant template from those provided on pages 143–150. You also need to complete justification sheets to justify your ideas.

- Select the treatment below that corresponds with your chosen commission.
- Complete the templates for your chosen treatment. Ensure that your ideas are an expansion of your pitch and proposal.

> Always check the extent that any treatment should detail (i.e. the length of any video or audio product, or number of pages or screens for any print-based, web-based or games product). Also check if your client has any templates they want you to follow, and any limits to the number of pages they want your treatment documentation to be.
>
> In the actual assessment some templates may be provided for your treatment, or you can use your own appropriate templates.

> This revision task will help you revise the skills that might be needed in your assessed task. The details of the actual assessed task may change so always make sure you are up to date. Ask your tutor or check the Pearson website for the most up-to-date Sample Assessment Material to get an idea of the structure of your assessed task and what this requires of you.

Treatment 1 – informational video

Create a storyboard using the templates provided to you that demonstrates:
- the opening 30 seconds of the video.

You may submit a maximum of six sheets: **three** storyboard sheets plus **three** justification sheets.

Treatment 2 – interactive website

Create a plan for the site including:
- navigation of the website as a whole
- diagrams/layout sheets for two linked pages from the site.

You may submit a maximum of six sheets: **three** diagrams/layout sheets (one site navigation sheet and two layout sheets) plus **three** justification sheets.

Treatment 3 – radio advertisement

Create a radio advert script for:
- a full 90-second commercial.

You may submit a maximum of six sheets: **three** script sheets plus **three** justification sheets.

Treatment 4 – poster campaign

Create a series of poster design sheets for:
- three A2 posters.

You may submit a maximum of six sheets: **three** poster layout sheets plus **three** justification sheets.

Treatment 5 – smartphone puzzle game

Create a visualisation for the game that shows:
- a screen layout for the menu screen
- the game screen for two levels of the game, including all onscreen content such as menu options, interface controls and icons.

You may submit a maximum of six sheets: **three** layout sheets plus **three** justification sheets.

> Go to the following pages to find the templates related to your chosen treatment:
> - Storyboard template – page 140
> - Webpage/layout template – page 141
> - Script template – page 143
> - Game layout template – page 146
> - Poster template – page 147
> - Justification sheet template – page 148

Example treatment

Below are examples of how you might respond to Commission 3 –radio advertisement, to practise your skills in completing a treatment.

The next two pages give an example of a treatment for commission 3. If this is relevant to your project you can complete the partial working below. If you want to respond to a different commission, have a go at producing a relevant treatment on separate paper, or on a computer. Make sure you meet the requirements outlined on the previous page. There are templates relevant to different media available on pages 140–148.

Remember that you should justify all your ideas in your justification sheet. You can practise this using the template on page 148.

> **Guided**

For a radio advertisement, a key part of the treatment will be tone of voice, speed and pauses in what is being said. Try to convey this in the script as much as possible and remember to justify it in your justification sheet, linking it to the commission.

Consider whether you would include any music in the piece and identify when this might start and finish within your script using square brackets in the text.

Time	Speaker	Script	Music / Sound effects
7 pm		Scene 1: Two flatmates are at home after work, eating TV dinner. Location: INT. On sofa in a living room	FX: Background noise of a football match on TV Music: Sports TV programme theme
	Daniel	Pass the brown sauce would you? [music starts] It's just not right eating sausages without a smothering of brown sauce is it?	
	Phil	Here you go [pause]. But take a look at the ingredients list. [pause]	
	Daniel	[music ends] Blimey! Have you seen how much sugar there is in one portion?	

Part of demonstrating the treatment of your idea for a radio script would be to clearly identify the scene (where it comes within the whole), the location and the time of day.

Think about any sound effects that you may need to include. Write these as they would appear using the format shown.

Using your planning, complete your templates for the particular commission you have chosen, bearing in mind as you go along what you will need to put in your justification sheet(s).

You now need to complete a justification sheet to support the script you have written.

Explain why you have chosen to set the piece where you have, and how this relates back to your set pitch, proposal and the overall commission itself.

Justification sheet ref (e.g. Storyboard page 1)	Producer	Title	Page number
Radio advertisement script page 1			1

I have chosen to set my radio advert on a weekday evening, with two flatmates eating their dinner in front of the TV after a day's work, to demonstrate an everyday situation that a lot of people aged 25–40 can relate to.

Daniel and Philip (the two speakers) are flatmates. They are talking about some of the ingredients in their TV dinner, in particular the amount of sugar contained in brown sauce. I have given them this spoken content to highlight the levels of sugar in many everyday foods, about which people within the target audience may be unaware.

> Explain who you have included in the piece and why you have given them the spoken content you have.

I have chosen to include the sound effects of a football match and a TV sporting theme tune to appeal to a large portion of the target audience (ages 25–40), and to demonstrate a typical activity of this target audience.

> Explain why you have decided to include sound effects and music and how this connects back to your target audience, the message you intended to convey and the aims of the client.

Now complete a justification sheet for your own chosen commission, justifying the choices you made in your treatment. Use the template provided on page 148.

END OF TASK

Revision task 2

To support your revision, this Workbook contains revision tasks to help you revise the skills that might be needed in your assessed task. The details of the actual assessed task may change so always make sure you are up to date. Ask your tutor or check the Pearson website for the most up-to-date Sample Assessment Material to get an idea of the structure of your assessed task and what this requires of you.

1 Formulating your ideas in response to a commission

1. Read the revision task information that follows carefully.
2. Analyse the information providedto help you to do this.
3. Choose **one** commission only for your response:
   - Commission 1 – Promotional video
   - Commission 2 – Website
   - Commission 3 – Audio podcast
   - Commission 4 – Leaflet
   - Commission 5 – Digital game
4. Generate and plan ideas in response to your chosen commission and medium using the information provided. You will need to plan material to allow you to create:
   - your rationale
   - your pitch
   - your proposal
   - your treatment

Task information

Start by reading the revision task information and supporting data. Remember that this is example task information only, and the organisation described is not real.

brightsparkssafety.com

You are a creative media production company. The press release below is from a potential client and is asking for responses to a commission. It comes from Bright Sparks, a charitable organisation that promotes road safety to children.

Press release from Bright Sparks

Bright Sparks is an independent charitable organisation set up to highlight to children and parents the importance of wearing luminescent and reflective clothing and accessories when it is dark.

The level of road accidents, injuries and child fatalities on UK roads continues to be a problem. Although overall the numbers of child casualties on our roads have gone down, it remains a significant issue, with 7807 pedestrians below the age of 16 being injured or killed on UK roads in 2011. Although accidents happen all year, the figures show that darker evenings in autumn and winter contribute to this toll, with drivers often unable to see children on darkened streets or roads if the children do not take safety precautions.

Bright Sparks educates young people about safe road use during darker evenings and provides easy access to reflective clothing and accessories that will ensure they stand out in lower light on the streets.

The current campaign focuses especially on young people aged 11–12, as they are particularly at risk because they are often walking to and from school unsupervised for the first time and may be less careful about their road use. This independent and style-conscious group may be less likely to wear safety-minded clothing or accessories. Bright Sparks therefore aims to produce materials that will appeal to this target group, instructing them without preaching or judging.

Bright Sparks is an independent and impartial organisation, receiving some government funding but mainly relying on funding from charitable organisations and businesses.

Supporting data

Accidental deaths among 5–14-year-olds

Road accidents account for over half of all
accidental deaths among 5–14-year-olds.

10-year-olds

11-year-olds

11- and 12-year-olds are most at risk, with an 11-year-old being
twice as likely to be seriously injured as a 10-year-old.

40% of secondary school pupils walk to school
without parental supervision.

Six out of ten 11–12-year-olds say they
have had a 'near miss' on the roads.

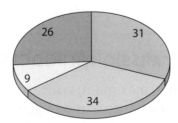

Children 11–12 years old

- I don't wear anything reflective.
- There is something on my bag or coat that is reflective.
- I wear something specifically because it is reflective.
- I have something reflective but don't wear it.

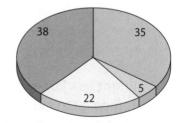

Children 11–12 years old

- I don't know why I need to wear reflective clothing.
- I've been told why I need to wear reflective clothing but have forgotten.
- I know why I need to wear reflective clothing and do so.
- I know why I need to wear reflective clothing but don't do so.

Now choose a revision commission that you would undertake, taking into account your own subject specialisms, skills and understanding.

REVISION COMMISSION 1: PROMOTIONAL VIDEO

Bright Sparks needs a short (six minutes, maximum) promotional video as part of our current campaign to raise awareness of the importance of road safety and promote the use of reflective clothing and accessories at night. The target audience is young people aged 11–12.

We expect this resource to be ready by early September to allow us to launch it as part of welcome week activities for new Year 7 pupils in secondary schools. Therefore, you will need to demonstrate that you have carefully considered the timescales and logistics of tackling this project.

We have sent this request to a number of different creative media production companies, so you will need to persuade us to take your idea forward in this competitive field.

We look forward to hearing from you.

REVISION COMMISSION 2: MOBILE PHONE-ACCESSIBLE INTERACTIVE WEBSITE

Bright Sparks needs a mobile phone-accessible interactive website (of at least five pages) as part of our current campaign to raise awareness of the importance of road safety and promote the use of reflective clothing and accessories at night. The target audience is young people aged 11–12.

We expect this resource to be ready by early September to allow us to launch it as part of welcome week activities for new Year 7 pupils in secondary schools. Therefore, you will need to demonstrate that you have carefully considered the timescales and logistics of tackling this project.

We have sent this request to a number of different creative media production companies, so you will need to persuade us to take your idea forward in this competitive field.

We look forward to hearing from you.

REVISION COMMISSION 3: PODCAST

Bright Sparks needs a short (six minutes, maximum) podcast as part of our current campaign to raise awareness of the importance of road safety and promote the use of reflective clothing and accessories at night. The target audience is young people aged 11–12.

We expect this resource to be ready by early September to allow us to launch it as part of welcome week activities for new Year 7 pupils in secondary schools. Therefore, you will need to demonstrate that you have carefully considered the timescales and logistics of tackling this project.

We have sent this request to a number of different creative media production companies, so you will need to persuade us to take your idea forward in this competitive field.

We look forward to hearing from you.

REVISION COMMISSION 4: LEAFLET

Bright Sparks needs a six-page colour leaflet (to be printed on two sides of A4) as part of our current campaign to raise awareness of the importance of road safety and promote the use of reflective clothing and accessories at night. The target audience is young people aged 11–12.

We expect this resource to be ready by early September to allow us to launch it as part of welcome week activities for new Year 7 pupils in secondary schools. Therefore, you will need to demonstrate that you have carefully considered the timescales and logistics of tackling this project.

We have sent this request to a number of different creative media production companies, so you will need to persuade us to take your idea forward in this competitive field.

We look forward to hearing from you.

REVISION COMMISSION 5: WEB-BASED PLATFORM GAME

Bright Sparks needs a web-based platform game (at least two levels) as part of our current campaign to raise awareness of the importance of road safety and promote the use of reflective clothing and accessories at night. The target audience is young people aged 11–12.

We expect this resource to be ready by early September to allow us to launch it as art of welcome week activities for new Year 7 pupils in secondary schools. Therefore, you will need to demonstrate that you have carefully considered the timescales and logistics of tackling this project.

We have sent this request to a number of different creative media production companies, so you will need to persuade us to take your idea forward in this competitive field.

We look forward to hearing from you.

Next, generate and plan ideas in response to your chosen commission and medium using the information provided. Make sure you make brief notes that cover your:
- rationale
- pitch
- proposal
- treatment.

You could refer back to the approaches taken on pages 110–125 in relation to the guided Revision Task 1 to help with your approach to Revision Task 2.

2 Responding to a commission

You must complete ALL sections.

To respond to the commission you will have read and analysed a brief and commission from a client, chosen a commission to respond to, planned ideas, and prepared for writing a commission response.

In the actual assessment:

- The brief and commissions will be new each year.
- You may not be allowed to use your preparatory notes, or there may be restrictions on the length and type of preparatory notes that are allowed.
- You will have a limited time in which to complete your commission response in the supervised assessment. Plan your time carefully to ensure you complete everything you need to within the allocated time.
- Some templates may be provided for your treatment, or you can use your own appropriate templates.

Check with your tutor or look at the latest Sample Assessment Material on the Pearson website for details.

Rationale

If you are asked to write a rationale, always check if there is a word limit.

To check the word limit in your supervised assessment, ask your tutor or check the most up-to-date Sample Assessment Material on the Pearson website.

 Links You can revise the skills needed for writing a rationale for moving image or print-based products on pages 172 and 173 of the Revision Guide. For more general advice, see page 150 of the Revision Guide.

Bright Sparks is looking for ideas that will meet the brief set and demonstrate that the data provided has been used to generate appropriate concepts.

Write a rationale explaining your ideas in response to the commission you have chosen. Bright Sparks will need to know how you used the information provided to develop your ideas. (Maximum 500 words.)

....

....

....

....

....

....

....

....

....

....

....

....

....

....

Continue your rationale on this page.

....
....
....
....
....
....
....
....
....
....
....
....
....
....
....
....
....
....
....
....
....
....
....
....
....
....
....
....
....

Pitch

Bright Sparks has sent this commission out to several production companies. You will therefore need to convince the client of the value of your proposed ideas in a succinct and persuasive way through a written pitch. You will need to 'sell' the idea by including an overview of the content and style of your proposed product to persuade them to choose your idea.

> If you are asked to write a pitch, always check if there is a word limit.
>
> To check the word limit in your supervised assessment, ask your tutor or check the most up-to-date Sample Assessment Material on the Pearson website.

> **Links** You can revise the skills needed for writing a pitch for moving image or print-based products on page 174 of the Revision Guide. For more general advice, see pages 151 and 152 of the Revision Guide.

Write a pitch to promote your idea to Bright Sparks in 350 words below.

....

....

....

....

....

....

....

....

....

....

....

....

....

....

....

....

....

....

....

....

Continue your pitch on this page.

....
....
....
....
....
....
....
....
....
....
....
....
....
....
....
....
....
....
....
....
....
....
....
....
....
....
....
....
....
....

Proposal

The proposal documents you present here are intended to expand on the idea you have generated and summarised in the pitch and should provide further detail about your proposed project. The proposal requires details of:

- content overview
- technical considerations
- contributors, assets, locations and equipment
- legal and ethical considerations
- scheduling and planning considerations.

Proposal (medium)	Producer (name)	Title of production	Page number

Content overview

....

....

....

....

....

....

....

....

....

....

....

....

....

....

....

....

....

....

....

....

> **Links** You can revise the skills needed for writing a content overview for moving image or print-based products on page 175 of the Revision Guide. For more general advice on writing a proposal see pages 154–157 of the Revision Guide.

Proposal (medium)	Producer (name)	Title of production	Page number

Technical considerations

....

....

....

....

....

....

....

....

....

....

....

....

....

....

....

....

....

....

....

....

....

....

....

....

....

....

Links You can revise the skills needed for writing about the technical considerations for moving image or print-based products on page 176 of the Revision Guide. For more general advice on writing a proposal see pages 154–157 of the Revision Guide.

Proposal (medium)	Producer (name)	Title of production	Page number

Contributors, assets, locations and equipment

....

....

....

....

....

....

....

....

....

....

....

....

....

....

....

....

....

....

....

....

....

....

....

....

....

Links You can revise the skills needed for writing about the project assets for moving image or print-based products on page 177 of the Revision Guide. For more general advice on writing a proposal see pages 154–157 of the Revision Guide.

Proposal (medium)	Producer (name)	Title of production	Page number

Legal and ethical considerations

....

....

....

....

....

....

....

....

....

....

....

....

....

....

....

....

....

....

....

....

....

....

....

....

....

....

Links You can revise the skills needed for writing about legal and ethical considerations for moving image or print-based products on page 178 of the Revision Guide. For more general advice on writing a proposal see pages 154–157 of the Revision Guide.

Proposal (medium)	Producer (name)	Title of production	Page number

Scheduling and planning considerations

....

....

....

....

....

....

....

....

....

....

....

....

....

....

....

....

....

....

....

....

....

....

....

....

Links You can revise the skills needed for writing about scheduling and planning considerations for moving image or print-based products on page 179 of the Revision Guide. For more general advice on writing a proposal see pages 154–157 of the Revision Guide.

Treatment

A treatment would include samples of how your final idea will look, sound and/or feel.

Bright Sparks has requested that you produce development documentation to help convey what the finished product will be like. You should use the templates provided and complete the accompanying justification sheets to justify your chosen ideas.

- Select the treatment below that corresponds with your chosen revision commission.
- Complete the templates required for your chosen treatment. Ensure that your ideas are an expansion of your pitch and proposal.

> Always check the extent that any treatment should detail (i.e. the length of any video or audio product, or number of pages or screens for any print-based, web-based or games product). Also check if your client has any templates they want you to follow, and any limits to the number of pages your client wants your treatment to be.
>
> In the actual assessment some templates may be provided for your treatment, or you can use your own appropriate templates.

Treatment 1 – promotional video

Create a storyboard that demonstrates:

- the opening 30 seconds of the video.

You may submit a maximum of six sheets: **three** storyboard sheets plus **three** justification sheets.

> This revision task will help you revise the skills that might be needed in your assessed task. The details of the actual assessed task may change so always make sure you are up to date. Ask your tutor or check the Pearson website for the most up-to-date Sample Assessment Material to get an idea of the structure of your assessed task and what this requires of you.

Treatment 2 – mobile-accessible interactive website

Create a plan for the site including:

- the navigation of the website as a whole
- diagrams/layout sheets for two linked pages from the site

You may submit a maximum of six sheets: **three** diagrams/layout sheets (one navigation sheet and two diagrams/layout sheets) plus **three** justification sheets.

Treatment 3 – podcast

Create a podcast script for:

- the first three minutes of your podcast.

You may submit a maximum of six sheets: **three** script sheets plus **three** justification sheets.

Treatment 4 – leaflet

Create a 'mocked up' leaflet for:

- both sides of a tri-fold A4 leaflet
- the copy (text) for one of the articles.

You may submit a maximum of six sheets: **two** layout sheets, **one** sample copy sheet plus **three** justification sheets.

Treatment 5: web-based platform game

Create a visualisation for the game that shows:

- a screen layout with details of how to access the menus and control interface
- storyboards of the first 15 seconds of introduction/gameplay.

You may submit a maximum of six sheets: **one** screen layout sheet and **two** storyboard sheets plus **three** justification sheets.

> Go to the following pages to find the templates related to your chosen treatment:
> - Storyboard template – page 140
> - Webpage/layout template – page 141
> - Web navigation template – page 142
> - Script template – page 143
> - Leaflet layout template – page 144
> - Sample copy template – page 145
> - Game layout template – page 146
> - Justification sheet template – page 148

END OF TASK

Storyboard template

Storyboard	Producer	Title	Page number

Image	Audio	Description
edit:		
		dur:
edit:		
		dur:
edit:		
		dur:
edit:		
		dur:
edit:		
		dur:

Webpage/layout template

Web page layout	Producer	Title	Page number

Web navigation template

Website navigation	Producer	Title	Page number

Website navigation	Producer	Title	Page number

Script template

Audio script		Producer	Title	Page number
Time	*Speaker*	*Script*		*Music/sound effects*

Leaflet layout template

Leaflet layout	Producer	Title	Page number

Sample copy template

Sample copy	Producer	Title	Page number

Game layout template

Game screen layout	Producer	Title	Page number

Game screen layout	Producer		Title	Page number

Poster layout template

Sample copy	Producer	Title	Page number

Sample copy	Producer	Title	Page number

Justification sheet template

Justification sheet ref. (e.g. Storyboard page 1)	Producer	Title	Page number

Justification sheet ref. (e.g. Storyboard page 1)	Producer	Title	Page number

Answers

Unit 1: Media Representations

Revision test 1 (page 2)

1 (a) The mother and child are wrapped in a red and gold blanket. These are both warm colours that create a sense of happiness, security and calm. This implies that using the fabric conditioner will also create these feelings.

(b) The text in the centre of the advertisement uses a handwritten font. The irregular letters give the impression that the text has been written by the child shown in the image. The contrast with the more formal fonts in other parts of the advertisement attracts our interest and encourages us to read it.

(c) Answers should include four of the following:
   • Brand logo and colour scheme
   • Slogan
   • Aims to be striking or memorable
   • More emphasis on images than words
   • Reliance on symbols and stereotypes

(d) Page layout should follow certain conventions so that readers are able to identify the most important elements of the page, which order to look at them and how to take action. The design must follow a clear, consistent visual hierarchy so that the reader can understand the message. In this advertisement, the eye is drawn to the large photo, which dominates the page. This image shows a calm, contented family, and is larger than the photo of the product itself in the bottom right-hand corner. This emphasises the possible result of using the product (happiness and comfort).
The rules of thirds is demonstrated by the faces, which are placed in the top half of the ad. The child-like handwriting font has the affect of placing an emotive message in the centre of the page.

(e) The advertisement features a large photo of a woman hugging a child, which we assume represents a mother and her daughter. They are clearly enjoying each other's company and sharing a quiet, happy moment together. This implies that this is the result of using the product being advertised, fabric conditioner, on the blanket they are wrapped in. The target audience for this advert is mothers. This has been chosen because they would aspire to this quiet, happy scene, and they are often the main family purchasers of laundry products that enable this purchase to happen.
The main text reads: 'It's more than a blanket; it's my secret power to make her smile'. This anchorage reinforces the message that the product will make mothers happy.
The absence of male figures from the scene suggests that only female caregivers are being targeted. Similarly, the selective representation of a mother and child sharing an intimate moment is likely to appeal most to other mothers.

2 (a) One example of intertextuality is the references to James Bond films, for example the portrayal of a confident, well-dressed man who drives a vintage sports car, and the jazz-influenced music score.

(b) 'The boss' is always seen wearing smart, expensive clothes – the first shot of him focuses on his designer leather shoe; he pays enough attention to detail to include a handkerchief in his breast pocket; and later he wears full evening dress. This positions him as rich and careful about the impression his appearance has on others. He makes eye contact with everyone he meets, suggesting he is confident about his senior position.

(c) Mulvey's theory of audience positioning states that men are often portrayed as active, leaders, strong and independent, all of which 'the boss' is shown to be. He is an 'alpha male', so both men and women do as he asks, and he has control over the manufacturing of both a traditionally masculine product (beer) and a sexualised feminine product (bras). He is, to some extent, objectified as the man living the ultimate male dream.

(d) In an oppositional reading, the decoder may understand the preferred meaning but reject it because their social position puts them in conflict with the preferred meaning. In this advertisement, the preferred meaning at first seems to be that the audience should aspire to the lifestyle of 'the boss', controlling the manufacture of products that men are often portrayed as desiring.
An oppositional reading may be that the viewer doesn't agree that this lifestyle is desirable, and thinks that 'the boss', in fact, leads an empty life dominated by work. He doesn't speak or directly interact with anyone beyond a nod, and he is shown as a loner, who doesn't even need, or want, to sleep.
Although the advertisement can be taken at face value, as portraying a desirable lifestyle, it is also open to oppositional readings. It can be viewed as a pastiche of portrayals of confident, powerful men, such as James Bond, and is clearly intended to be humorous. When 'the boss' winks at the end, we are led to question our previous assumptions and consider whether he is making us complicit in his lifestyle, or whether he is implying that perhaps his life isn't quite what it seems.

3 (a) Side lighting.

(b) Side lighting gives a three-dimensional appearance and adds drama. This striking opening shot engages the viewer's attention at once. The black and white contrast of the man's face highlights his intense focus on what is revealed in the next shot to be a barrel.

(c) The music.

(d) The pub is represented as welcoming and relaxed, where people go to have a good time. This is established through both diegetic and non-diegetic sound – the laughter of the pub customers and the gentle, folk-influenced sound track. The music is initially muffled while the man is in the cellar but, as he opens the door and enters the heart of the pub, it becomes clear, drawing the viewer into the pub's atmosphere. The lighting in the pub is soft, with a yellow tinge, reinforcing the relaxed, warm feel of the bar. Most of the customers are backlit and in semi-shadow, helping to create a sense of intimacy.

(e) Neither man speaks; however, we get a clear idea of their characters. 'The boss' is calm, confident and smartly dressed. He is powerful because he can instruct others to do his bidding with just a nod or gesture. We assume that the man in the Greene King ad is also a boss, perhaps the landlord of the pub, but, unlike 'the boss' in the Cobra ad, his position is implied by his presence in an area nobody else enters, the pub cellars, and by the front-on, eye-level shot of him walking through the crowded bar.

Unlike the Cobra boss, whose costume of expensive suits implies he is of a higher social class than those around him, the Greene King boss is dressed similarly to those around him, suggesting he is 'one of them'.

Both men seem to take special care of the products they are in charge of – the Cobra boss directs the detailed production of beer and bars, while the Greene King boss personally prepares the barrel of beer he is about to serve. Both men are portrayed apart from the people around them and appear alone in either the opening shot (Greene King) or the closing shot (Cobra). This reinforces their position as experts, single-handedly providing products to please others. However, both men seem to be content, showing satisfied facial expressions even though they are not participating in the activity around them.

4 (a) The dominant colour in the apartment scenes is gold. The walls, decorations and other props are gold, as are Delysia's dressing gown and hair. This colour implies wealth and opulence, suggesting that Delysia is rich. The warmth of the colour also suggests comfort and relaxation. In contrast, Miss Pettigrew's clothing and hair are brown and dull. This suggests she does not fit into this world.

(b) The first shots of Miss Pettigrew suggest she is depressed and downtrodden. Her figure expression is downcast – she looks worried and walks with her head down. Her costume is a drab dark brown, her hair is untidy and she appears to be wearing no make-up. This implies that she is poor and has other worries than her appearance. This is reinforced by the contrast with glamorous Delysia. Miss Pettigrew displays a shocked, disapproving expression several times while in Delysia's apartment, suggesting she is not comfortable with Delysia's lifestyle. However, she can also be rebellious, for example by smoking the cigar left behind by Delysia's lover.

(c) Over-shoulder shot (or over the shoulder shot).

(d) It is used to show two characters talking and draws the audience into the conversation. It can also provide extra information about what is happening by showing body language and the distance between the characters.

(e) Possible answers could be:
  • romantic comedy
  • comedy
  • farce.

(f) Answers depend on genre chosen but examples could be:
Romantic comedy:
  • Verbal and physical humour
  • Character-driven
  • Lovers kept apart by obstacles
  • Man and woman kiss
  • Warm lighting
  • Urban setting
  • Editing that dwells on a humorous line of dialogue or event
  • No violent or distressing scenes shown
Farce:
  • Verbal and physical humour, e.g. falling over sofa
  • Improbable plot
  • Protagonist at odds with the environment
  • Exaggerated characters
  • Social transgressions
  • Rapid exits and entrances
  • Excessive use of props and costumes for comedic value.

(g) The film is set in the 1930s, when expectations of how a woman should behave were different. 'Ladylike' behaviour may be to expect women to take care over their physical appearance, to defer to men, and to take a passive role. Several shots in the trailer reinforce this, for example:
  • Delysia's glamour, femininity and willingness to defer to men appear to be directly related to her apparent wealth and success.
  • Several men in the trailer tell Delysia how she should behave.
  • Delysia's unladylike sexual availability seems to be punished by a chaotic lifestyle.
  • Miss Pettigrew does not visually fulfil expectations of feminine appearance, and is punished for this via unemployment and poverty.
  • After Miss Pettigrew's makeover, she seems visually happier and she is rewarded by male attention, for example she drops a cake in shock after a man compliments her appearance.
  • Delysia's line 'Men are so untrusting – I can't think why' appears to be ironic as the audience is expected to think that she is untrustworthy.
Examples of how the trailer subverts this:
  • Delysia's lifestyle seems superficial and she seems unhappy (e.g. eyes filling with tears) in later scenes.
  • Miss Pettigrew, the less feminine character, appears to take control of the situation, even after her makeover to become more feminine.
  • Miss Pettigrew is willing to break with conventions of feminine behaviour (e.g. when questioned about girls smoking cigars, Miss Pettigrew responds 'if I want to smoke cigars, I'll damned well smoke cigars' and does so; she tells a character to 'sock him in the jaw', which he does). The audience is expected to respond positively to these transgressions.
  • Delysia describes Miss Pettigrew's new appearance, which has involved intensive changes, as 'as nature intended'. This humorous, ironic line implies that it is not easy to be 'ladylike' and that in fact feminine ideals are constructed.

Revision test 2 (page 12)

1 (a) Over-shoulder shot (or over the shoulder shot).
  (b) Indicative answer:
    • Used to show two characters talking.
    • Relates the characters' interaction with each other.
    • Provides extra information through body language and distance – in the case of this clip, to show that Sue and Angela are not communicating well, as Angela isn't looking at Sue.
    • Draws audience into the conversation.

2 (a) Indicative content:
    • Sue is portrayed as a stereotypical harassed mother – downcast figure expression; stressed tone of voice; dialogue in which she emphasises her responsibilities.
    • Angela is a stereotypical middle-class, middle-aged woman – colourful clothes, eager to please, unwilling to take on additional responsibilities that will tie her down.
  (b) Indicative content:
    • The family lives in suburbia (indicated by the external/establishing shot of well-kept houses).
    • The family is having a semi-formal dinner party, which is often associated with affluence and eagerness to reinforce social standing.
    • All characters speak in received pronunciation, with no obvious regional accent or slang.
    • The family seem to have a reasonable income, for example the house is comfortably furnished with good-quality furniture and computers.

3 Indicative content:

Angela:
- Dressed in flowing clothes with splashes of colour, suggesting her outgoing personality and relative freedom.
- Large necklace suggests a larger-than-life, confident personality.
- Seems emotionally disturbed as she describes their father's erratic behaviour, not meeting Sue's eyes.
- Appears nervous, speaking quickly, with a bustling manner and moving her eyes from Pete to Sue and back as she speaks.
- Doesn't make eye-contact when she knows her sister wants to argue with her.
- Portrays her sister as 'a mean, suburban, small-minded bitch'.

Sue:
- Conservatively and practically dressed in plain black, suggesting a more retiring and conventional personality than Angela.
- Small necklace suggests a less confident personality.
- Appears tired, with slow, deliberate actions and unblinking when looking at Angela.
- Appears downbeat, negative and stressed, for example by using emphatic body language.
- Anxious about dealing with her children.
- Portrays her sister as flighty, unrealistic and immature ('a rucksack of self-help books and an addiction to tofu').

Both women are emphatic about getting their point across.

4 (a) Indicative content:
- The women have been shouting abuse at each other, so the long pause when Karen appears seems intensified.
- The sudden silence increases the drama of the moment.
- Sue's gaze switches from Angela, who is in front of her at her eye level, to Karen, who is to the side and lower because of her height.
- It is also a comic moment, as Karen, with her toy hippo, has interrupted a serious argument, which is an awkward moment for the two women as they review what they have been saying.

(b) Indicative content:
- Karen is carrying a toy hippo, a prop associated with childhood, comfort and innocence.
- She has come into the scene silently, while the women were shouting.
- The women have been shouting personal abuse at each other, so Karen's request for a snack breaks the argument's cycle.
- The women are wearing black and dark blue clothes, associated with darkness and evil, while Karen is in light-coloured pyjamas.

5 (a) Establishing shot.

(b) • This is a long shot used at the opening of a scene to show the setting. We see that the action takes place in a terraced house at night.
- It provides us with a context for the action, and also breaks up the sequence of interior shots.
- The previous scene shows Pete intervening in the argument and Sue putting her son back to bed. It demonstrates time passing.

6 Indicative content:
- It is night-time and the family are holding a dinner party, so this is likely to be a realistic lighting choice in such a setting.
- Low key lighting has less fill lighting than key lighting so creates more shadows.
- It emphasises dark, grey and black tones.
- It emphasises emotional intensity, in keeping with the dramatic argument.
- The contrast between light and dark areas creates a sense of drama and tension.
- It conveys mystery, tension, alienation, foreboding and threat.

7 Indicative content:
- Traditionally, sitcoms have a laughter track or live studio audience, but this does not, so there is no guidance for the viewer on when to laugh.
- Although comedies often have serious elements, they are usually resolved by the end. The sisters' issues are not resolved in this clip.
- The comic relief from the drama is subtle, for example Pete trying to make polite conversation with his guests while the women can be heard shouting in the kitchen. It is the awkward social situation that is funny, rather than his exact words.
- The clip has elements of the documentary genre, with a handheld camera and scenes fading out rather than ending definitively.
- In some ways, the clip actually reinforces comedy genre conventions, for example by portraying larger-than-life characters; however, they are placed in a realistic setting and situation.

8 Indicative content:

Examples of Pete appearing stressed but well-meaning:
- Pete appears to be anxious to maintain the social order, for example by trying to pretend to his guests that nothing is out of the ordinary when clearly it is.
- He seems to have little control over the action, reactively responding to other characters' behaviour.
- He is shown participating in parenting tasks, for example engaging with his sons.
- He acts as mediator in the argument, albeit belatedly.

Possible oppositional or negotiated meanings:
- Pete is not proactive in defending his family, for example he does not actively defend his wife's point of view and doesn't intervene in the argument until the end of the clip.
- When he does finally intervene, it is his wife's name that he shouts, rather than his sister-in-law's, presumably because he feels she should be behaving better in their house. He then continues to address Sue as he complains about the argument, ignoring Angela.
- He criticises his wife in front of their son, agreeing with him that 'it is unfair to shout all the way through dinner when we've got guests'.
- He insists that Sue puts their son back to bed rather than doing it himself, which could either be seen as avoiding his parental responsibility or as a way of separating the sisters.
- The scene ends as Pete looks at Angela for the first time, but we do not see or hear what he says to her.

9 Indicative content:
- All the characters are smartly dressed – even the boy is wearing a shirt – suggesting that this is a special occasion. This makes Sue and Angela's behaviour more embarrassing and amusing.
- There is a long pause in the dialogue at the start of the scene, as the people at the table overhear the sisters arguing in the kitchen. This is presented as an awkward social situation, as everyone avoids each other's eyes or fidgets with props such as glasses and napkins.
- When the dialogue does start, it is stilted, as the speakers are obviously trying hard to find something to say. The accompanying figure expression (body language) of Pete and Ravi highlights their embarrassment, which intensifies the humour.
- The reaction of other characters to Jake leaving the room suggests that they would like to do the same.
- Pete pursuing the boring topic of Ravi's office layout is clearly intended to be humorous – his frequent pauses reinforce this, as he desperately tries to save the evening. The audience may consider what they would do in that situation.

10 Indicative content:
- Many technical aspects of this clip are more common in a factual programme than a sitcom.
- Elements of a documentary style used in the clip include:
  - handheld camera work
  - eye-level shots
  - overlapping dialogue
  - some apparently unscripted dialogues/monologues
  - shots lingering on faces and rooms when no action is taking place
  - dwelling on fairly mundane details of family life
  - lack of a laughter track or any other non-diegetic sound.
- Elements of a standard (fictional) sitcom or drama include:
  - all scenes taking place in a confined space (the house), which suggests they are filmed in a studio
  - jokes and humour every few seconds
  - a familiar plot of an awkward social situation
  - characters having private conversations that they would be unlikely to have if they knew a camera was present.

11 Indicative content:
- Pete and Sue reinforce the ideological norm of a heterosexual couple facing and solving problems in order to raise their children as well as they can.
- They may be regarded as relatable because they encounter the types of issue that couples often face in real life, for example dealing with family issues, disagreeing with other family members, looking after their children.
- Both are defined through their status as parents.
- Sue reinforces the stereotype of the put-upon mother, but she and her sister also reinforce the stereotype of warring siblings.
- Sue and Pete are in a committed relationship, reinforcing an apparent assumption that two cohabiting parents is the best combination for bringing up children.
- Angela's different attitude to responsibility represents the stereotypical 'black sheep of the family'.
- Sue, Pete and their three children never appear together in this clip, which could suggest the fragmentation of modern family life.
- The extended family has a role in everyday life – Angela and Sue argue over the care of their father. That this is an important topic is portrayed as the norm.
- The documentary-style production enhances the realism of the representation, implying that this is a real and therefore typical family.
- The clip challenges sitcom convention by not solving all the problems tidily at the end of the episode, suggesting that families have to face ongoing issues in real life.
- Even though the family are clearly comfortably off and middle-class, the episode opposes typical assumptions by clearly showing that this doesn't stop them from having problems.

Unit 3: Digital Media Skills

Revision task brief (page 20)

1 Example answer:
The target audience is young people who are planning to go on to higher education or enter work.

2 Example answers:
1 Easy to use/manage on the move
2 No fee
3 Overdraft facility available

3 Example answers:
1 Available 24 hours a day, seven days a week
2 Interest can be earned on credit balances

4 Example answers:
Keeping information about their finances secure. Having access to online banking. Sharing their financial details with other people.

5 Example answers:
1 Do not use obvious passwords (e.g. your birthday)
2 Shred bills/bank statements
3 Never share your password

Revision media brief 1: video product (page 21)

1 Learner's own response.
2 Example answers:
1 Video camera
2 Tripod
3 Lights
4 Editing software
5 Microphone
3 Example answers:
1 Interviews with students on how they manage their finances.
2 A short cautionary tale of how someone lost money from their bank account by not following basic security considerations.
3 Interviews with bank staff about how bank accounts work.

Revision media brief 2: audio product (page 22)

1 Learner's own response.
2 Example answers:
1 Portable recorder
2 Microphone
3 Editing software
4 Headphones
5 Mixer
3 Example answers:
1 A music-based programme with segments of financial advice.
2 Interviews with students on how they manage their finances.
3 A podcast.

Revision media brief 3: website (page 23)

1 Learner's own response.
2 Answers will depend on the websites chosen.
3 Example answers:
1 A web page on keeping personal data secure using colourful and engaging graphics.
2 An interactive quiz on how to set up a bank account.
3 An animation demonstrating various ways of keeping financial information secure.

Revision media brief 4: digital e-magazine (page 24)

1 Learner's own response.
2 Example answers:
1 Digital camera
2 Word processing software
3 Layout software
4 Image editing software
5 Internet access software to find audiovisual sourced material
3 Example answers:
1 An interactive quiz on how to set up a bank account.
2 A feature on keeping personal data secure using colourful and engaging graphics.
3 An interview with a financial expert.

Revision media brief 5: digital game (page 25)

1 Learner's own response.
2 Example answers:
   1 A games engine
   2 Voice/sound recorder
   3 Microphone
   4 Asset manipulation software
   5 Asset modelling software
3 Example answers:
   1 A reward game where points are given for making personal data secure.
   2 An interactive game where players are able to see how their choices can affect their finances.
   3 A role play game that demonstrates effective management of finances.

Generating ideas and logging assets

Media brief 1: video product (page 27)

1 Answers could include:

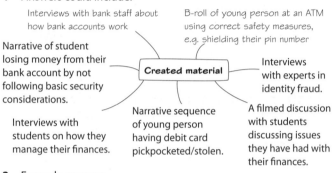

2 Example answers:
   • Library footage about statistics on financial fraud.
   • Appropriate background music.
   • Video from news or financial websites.
3 (a) Learner's own response.
   (b) Example answer:
   Dear Mrs Lloyd,
   I have been commissioned to produce a short film for a project entitled 'Your Finances'. The aim of this project is to provide support and guidance on financial matters to young people who are planning to go on to higher education or to enter work.
   I think the audience would really benefit from your advice and guidance, and so I would love to come in and film a short interview with you.
   I'd be most grateful if you would get back to me to let me know if you would be willing to talk to me on camera.
   Thank you.
   Yours sincerely,
4 Learner's own response.
5 Learner's own response, completing the table format provided.

Media brief 2: audio product (page 29)

1 Answers could include:

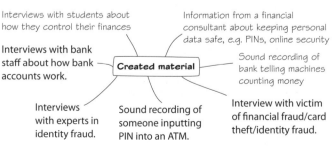

2 Example answers:
   • Library audio clip about statistics on financial fraud.
   • Appropriate background music.
   • Audio from news or financial websites.
3 (a) Learner's own response.
   (b) Example answer:
   Dear Mrs Lloyd,
   I have been commissioned to produce a short audio piece for a project entitled 'Your Finances'. The aim of this project is to provide support and guidance on financial matters to young people who are planning to go on to higher education or to enter work.
   I think the audience would really benefit from your advice and guidance, and so I would love to come in and record a short interview with you.
   I'd be most grateful if you would get back to me to let me know if you would be willing to talk to me and to be recorded.
   Thank you.
   Yours sincerely,
4 Learner's own response.
5 Learner's own response, completing the table format provided.

Media brief 3: website (page 31)

1 Answers could include:

2 Example answers:
   • Information from a website with statistics on financial fraud.
   • Library stock photos related to money/finance/banks.
   • Library stock digital graphics.
3 (a) Learner's own response.
   (b) Example answer:
   Dear Mrs Lloyd,
   I have been commissioned to produce a website for a project entitled 'Your Finances'. The aim of this project is to provide support and guidance on financial matters to young people who are planning to go on to higher education or to enter work.
   I think the audience would really benefit from your advice and guidance, and so I would love to come in and talk to you to gather information for a page which will advise students on managing their money.
   I'd be most grateful if you would get back to me to let me know if you would be willing to talk to me.
   Thank you.
   Yours sincerely,
4 Learner's own response.
5 Learner's own response, completing the table format provided.

Media brief 4: digital e-magazine (page 33)

1 Answers could include:

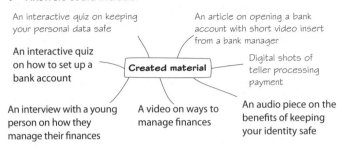

2 Example answers:
- Information from a website with statistics on financial fraud.
- Library stock photos related to money/finance/banks.
- Newspaper and magazine articles.

3 (a) Learner's own response.
   (b) Example answer:

Dear Mrs Lloyd,
I have been commissioned to produce a digital e-magazine for a project entitled 'Your Finances'. The aim of this project is to provide support and guidance on financial matters to young people who are planning to go on to higher education or to enter work.
I think the audience would really benefit from your advice and guidance, and so I would love to come in and record a short interview with you (either video or audio) to gather information from you for the project.
I'd be most grateful if you would get back to me to let me know if you would be willing to talk to me and to be recorded.
Thank you.
Yours sincerely,

4 Learner's own response.

5 Learner's own response, completing the table format provided.

Media brief 5: digital game (page 35)

1 Answers could include:

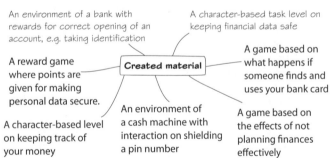

2 Example answers:
- Library/stock games characters.
- Appropriate background music.
- Library/stock sound effects.

3 (a) Learner's own response.
   (b) Example answer:

Dear Mrs Lloyd,
I have been commissioned to produce a digital game for a project entitled 'Your Finances'. The aim of this project is to provide support and guidance on financial matters to young people who are planning to go on to higher education or to enter work.
I think the audience would really benefit from your advice and guidance, and so I would love to come in and talk to you about online banking security to gather information from you to help me develop the game.
I'd be most grateful if you would get back to me to let me know if you would be willing to talk to me.
Thank you.
Yours sincerely,

4 Learner's own response.

5 Learner's own response, completing the table format provided.

Preparing assets and providing evidence

Media brief 1: video product (page 38)

1 Learner's own response, but could include references to:
- changing the colour of the background
- changing the overall colour balance.

2 Learner's own response, but could include references to:
- removing unwanted footage
- shortening scenes.

3 Learner's own response, but could include references to:
- making the sound level all the way through the piece
- removing any extraneous noise.

4 Learner's own response, but could include references to:
- creating titles/credits that stand out
- having titles and credits that are appropriate for the style of the piece
- making tiles/credits that scroll.

5 Learner's own response, but could include references to:
- an asset that needs to be cropped
- an asset that needs to shortened
- an asset that needs to have extraneous material removed.

6 Learner's own response.

7 Learner's own response.

Media brief 2: audio product (page 40)

1 Learner's own response, but could include references to:
- making the sound level all the way through the piece
- removing any extraneous noise.

2 Learner's own response, but could include references to:
- editing to remove unwanted material
- editing for length.

3 Learner's own response, but could include references to making the sound balance correct between voice and sound effects.

4 Learner's own response, but could include references to:
- making credits audible
- ensuring the tiles/credits are accurate in terms of names and job titles.

5 Learner's own response, but could include references to:
- ensuring that a backup file is kept
- naming files appropriately
- making appropriate file folders.

6 Learner's own response.

7 Learner's own response.

Media brief 3: website (page 42)

1 Learner's own response, but could include references to:
- changing text size to avoid clashes with the background
- updated designs in light of the client's needs.

2 Learner's own response, but could include references to:
- changing colours to avoid clashing with background
- blending colours to make a seamless design.

3 Learner's own response, but could include references to:
- cutting copy to fit
- language level
- font size
- font format (e.g. bold for emphasis)

4 Learner's own response, but could include references to:
- making sure the buttons work
- ensuring the interactive elements are appropriate for the topic.

5 Learner's own response, but could include references to:
- ensuring that a backup file is kept
- naming files appropriately
- making appropriate file folders.

6 Learner's own response.

7 Learner's own response.

Media brief 4: digital e-magazine (page 44)

1 Learner's own response, but could include references to:
   - cropping to focus on one part of an image
   - resizing to fit.
2 Learner's own response, but could include references to:
   - changing colours to avoid clashing with background
   - blending colours to make a seamless design
   - making sure that the digital graphics fit the house style of the e-magazine.
   Learner's own response, but could include references to:
   - cutting copy to fit
   - language level
   - style – formal/informal.
4 Learner's own response, but could include references to:
   - changing copy by including a link to another page in the e-magazine
   - adapting an image to include a play button that links to a video piece
   - adapting a graphic to make it link to another page in the e-magazine, by having a link in the graphic that the reader can see and click on.
5 Learner's own response, but could include references to:
   - planning a page to ensure readability
   - ensuring that the page appears 'clean' and not cluttered.
6 Learner's own response.
7 Learner's own response.

Media brief 5: digital game (page 46)

1 Learner's own response, but could include references to:
   - making the character small to emphasise scale
   - changing the personality of the character to fit with the 'mood' of the game.
2 Learner's own response, but could include references to:
   - changing the background colour to emphasise 'mood'
   - changing the scene to ensure the player understands their environment.
3 Learner's own response, but could include references to:
   - making the characters work within the environment
   - making the story work in terms of rewards and game play by making the characters engage with their environment.
4 Learner's own response, but could include references to:
   - changing the 'mood' using appropriate music
   - changing the game by adding sound effects
   - adding voice where necessary.
5 Learner's own response, but could include references to:
   - adapting an existing environment
   - adapting an existing character.
6 Learner's own response.
7 Learner's own response.

Creating and storing your media product

Media brief 1: video product (page 49)

1 Learner's own response.
2 Learner's own response.
3 Learner's own response, but should allow enough time within the deadline for feedback, incorporating changes and re-testing.
4 Learner's own response.
5 Learner's own response, but should relate back to the brief and include references to:
   - running time
   - professional standards
   - fitness for purpose (e.g. for target audience)
   - quality of shot material
   - quality of editing.

Media brief 2: audio product (page 51)

1 Learner's own response.
2 Learner's own response.
3 Learner's own response, but should allow enough time within the deadline for feedback, incorporating changes and re-testing.
4 Learner's own response.
5 Learner's own response, but should relate back to the brief and include references to:
   - running time
   - professional standards
   - fitness for purpose (e.g. for target audience)
   - quality of recorded materials
   - quality of editing.

Media brief 3: website (page 53)

1 Learner's own response.
2 Learner's own response.
3 Learner's own response, but should allow enough time within the deadline for feedback, incorporating changes and re-testing.
4 Learner's own response.
5 Learner's own response, but should relate back to the brief and include references to:
   - extent/size
   - professional standards
   - fitness for purpose (e.g. for target audience)
   - quality of graphics
   - quality of interaction (speed, download time).

Media brief 4: digital e-magazine (page 55)

1 Learner's own response.
2 Learner's own response.
3 Learner's own response, but should allow enough time within the deadline for feedback, incorporating changes and re-testing.
4 Learner's own response.
5 Learner's own response, but should relate back to the brief and include references to:
   - extent/size
   - professional standards
   - fitness for purpose (e.g. for target audience)
   - quality of images used
   - quality of text used
   - interactive elements usability.

Media brief 5: digital game (page 57)

1 Learner's own response.
2 Learner's own response.
3 Learner's own response, but should allow enough time within the deadline for feedback, incorporating changes and re-testing.
4 Learner's own response.
5 Learner's own response, but should relate back to the brief and include references to:
   - extent/running time
   - professional standards
   - fitness for purpose (e.g. for target audience)
   - quality of characters
   - quality of environment
   - quality of game play.

Unit 5: Specialist Subject Investigation

1 Research

Revision task 1: Task information (pages 67–72)

1   Example answer:
   - Page 1 of the article: Introduction/executive summary – 'Integration' means inclusion or absorption – in this case social networking has become included in people's lives to the extent it is 'absorbed' (it is not noticed as a separate thing).
   - Page 1 of the article: Introduction/executive summary – the examples of social networking sites and their function seem out of date. More up-to-date examples are Twitter, Instagram and Snapchat, which are used to share short messages (up to 140 characters) and links to news stories, websites and photos, and interact with other users (Twitter); and to share photos and videos (Instagram, Snapchat).
   (Learner will then make their own further notes.)

2   Example answers:
   - **When was the research undertaken?**
     The research was undertaken between July and December 2007.
   - **Is the research source reliable?**
     The research source is reliable – Ofcom is a government-approved regulatory authority.
   - **What qualitative research methods have been used?**
     The qualitative research methods that have been used are: qualitative face-to-face survey; face-to-face computer-assisted personal interviewing survey and face-to-face home interviews.
   - **What quantitative research methods have been used?**
     The quantitative research methods that has been used is a continuous face-to-face survey.
   - **Are there any gaps in the research findings?**
     Possible gaps in the research findings include: exploration of gender differences, out-of-date examples of social networking sites, lack of representation of non-users of social networking sites.

3   Learner's own response – should relate to their chosen media sector and any issues they have identified within the article.

4   Learner's own response. Additional items could include:
   - Primary research: use the relevant social networking site to interact with users and ask them questions
   - Secondary research: literature review of scholarly articles about the use of different networking sites

5   Learner's own response, depending on media sector chosen. Must include notes from at least one primary and one secondary method of research, as well as research based on the article.

6   Learner's own response, depending on own research undertaken.

7   Learner's own response, depending on own notes.

8   Learner's own response, depending on media sector chosen. Additional items could include:
   - Ofcom (2015) Report on internet safety measures: Strategies of parental protection for children online. [Online] Available at: https://www.ofcom.org.uk/__data/assets/pdf_file/0020/31754/Fourth-internet-safety-report.pdf.
   - Personal interview, Interview 8, User of Instagram (age 19), Interviewed 12/04/16 (transcript).
   - Personal interview, Interview 3, User of Twitter (age 34), Interviewed 5/04/16 (transcript).
   - Taylor, R. (2014) Making social networking a real-life reality [Online] Available at: http://www.bbc.co.uk/news/technology-29622611
   - Wakefield, J. (2016). Social media 'outstrips TV' as news source for young people. [Online] Available at: http://www.bbc.co.uk/news/uk-36528256

2 Revision activities (pages 73–78)

1   Learner's own response, but could include reference to:
   The key issues are:
   - Use of social networking is growing rapidly, especially among teenagers and young adults (49% of 8–17-year-olds and 54% of 16–24-year-olds).
   - There is a significant lack of awareness about privacy and safety issues on social networking sites and their risks – 41% of children with visible profiles have them visible to public, and 44% of adults; 25% of users have posted sensitive details on their profiles (rising to 34% in 16–24-year-olds).
   - Younger adults (aged 16–24) more likely to communicate with strangers via social networking.
   - Significant number of under-13s have social networking profiles (18% of 8–11-year-olds).
   The article uses quantitative research methods as the findings have been collated from three months of continuous face-to-face survey data (2235 respondents).
   The article uses qualitative research methods as the findings have been collated from qualitative face-to-face surveys (39 users + 13 non-users = 52 total), face-to-face computer-assisted personal interviewing surveys (653 parents + 653 children + 279 non-parents = 1585 total), and face-to-face in-home interviews (2905 interviewees).

2   Learner's own response, but should relate own research findings to the key issues they identified, and the conclusions of the article.

3   Answer will depend on media sector chosen and own research undertaken. For the TV sector, answers could include reference to:
   - users following similar groups, such as TV programmes, TV personalities, News programmes (on Facebook pages, Twitter, etc.)
   - own questionnaire results and research may confirm that younger people aged 14–18 use social media sites such as Facebook, Instagram, Snapchat and Twitter in order to follow/interact with their idols and their personal lives, keep up to date with soap opera storylines, watch clips, trailers, episodes, etc.
   - other impacts on TV could be that fewer people watch TV live – they consume their TV through social networking sites.

4   Answer will depend on media sector chosen and own research undertaken, but could include:
   - if/how international experience has influenced consumption in TV, games, radio, etc.
   - how international experience has impacted education sectors (e.g. HE, other CPD, courses such as languages, specific skill sets required for overseas)
   - if/how international experience has increased likelihood of travelling or booking additional trips.

5   Answer will depend on own research undertaken, but could include:
   - statistics of what consumers are purchasing (e.g. TV packages, international channels, bespoke memberships)
   - questionnaires with HE students regarding career plans in the UK/abroad, gap years, internships
   - surveys in local area with secondary school learners or FE regarding the access to international trips
   - travel agent research and survey results (existing research).

Revision task 2: Task information

1 Research (pages 87–93)

Read the task information and identify issues

Learner's own response. Key words should be highlighted or underlined, and possibly some annotation to show understanding their meaning. Key dates/themes may also be annotated to indicate further research. Key terms/areas of interest may be annotated to indicate further research and how they may do this.

Analyse the task information and plan and undertake your research

Learner's own response. As above, including any references (e.g. web addresses and access dates).

Summarise your notes and findings

Learner's own response, but must:
- include the key areas and areas for further research identified
- include reference to own research
- be wholly relevant and link directly to the article and associated factors
- list a maximum of ten primary and ten secondary sources, correctly referenced.

2 Revision activities (pages 94–98)

1 Learner's own response, but could include reference to:
   Key issues:
   - Large majority of people with international experience described themselves as having abilities needed for innovation.
   - Access to a range of activities is vital in reaping the full benefits of international experience.
   - Vast majority of those with international experience felt it helped them to develop a number of skills considered important to the contemporary workplace.
   - Seven out of ten were confident communicators, able to work well with people from other countries and cultures.
   - Respondents with international experience were more likely to report that they had: strong analytical and critical thinking skills (73%); problem-solving skills (83%); a creative mindset (66%).
   - Lack of public and consistent data available (so, challenging to gain comprehensive overview of scale, nature and impact of opportunities, and meaningful comparison between UK and other countries is virtually impossible).
   - Those offering international opportunities need to better understand what makes a more powerful experience and actively promote the development of appropriate opportunities.
   The article uses quantitative research methods as findings have been collated from a survey of 1148 UK residents, as well as literature reviews.
   The article uses qualitative research methods as the findings have been collated from semi-structured interviews with individuals, and case studies of a range of programmes that enable people to develop international experience.

2 Learner's own response, but should relate own research findings to the key issues they identified, and the conclusions of the article.

3 Answer will depend on media sector chosen and own research undertaken.

4 Answer will depend on media sector chosen and own research undertaken. Should have a direct link to the influence of international experiences and how these have influenced consumption. For example, in film an individual may subscribe to a bespoke international publication based on a trip to a film festival, or they may continue to attend additional international film events.

5 Answer will depend on own research undertaken, but could include:
   - statistics of what consumers are purchasing (e.g. TV packages, international channels, bespoke memberships)
   - questionnaires with HE students regarding career plans in the UK/abroad, gap years, internships
   - surveys in local area with secondary school learners or FE regarding the access to international trips
   - travel agent research and survey results (existing research)
   - international magazine/journal subscriptions
   - website subscriptions.

Unit 8: Responding to a Commission

Revision task 1

1. Formulating ideas in response to a commission (pages 101–102)

1 Answer should include references to:
   - Promoting health and fitness among the UK population.
   - Promoting healthy lifestyles.
   - To focus on people aged 25–40.
   - To inform and support, rather than dictate or be judgemental.

2 Answer should include references to:
   - How a lack of physical activity can contribute to heart problems.
   - The risk factors and impact of unhealthy lifestyle choices.
   - Advising and encouraging healthy choices.
   - Alerting younger people about possible long-term damage caused by choices earlier in life.

3 Answer should include references to:
   - Wanting to inform and support people, rather than dictate to them or seem to be judgemental.
   - Providing education and guidance.
   - Providing positive and proactive advice.
   - Wanting to be seen as a helping hand for making decisions about lifestyles.

4 Its funding comes from a mix of government, charitable and business sources.

5 They are hoping to reach people age 25–40 who live in the UK.

6 Learner's own response, depending on the commission chosen.

Task information (page 103)

1 30 per cent of all adults in the UK have high blood pressure.

2 41,000 people under 75 die from cardiovascular disease each year.

3 40 per cent of 30-year-olds surveyed in 2016 do between 30 minutes and 1 hour of exercise a day.

4 The percentage difference between 1986 (at 72 per cent) and 2016 (at 40 per cent) is 32 per cent lower.

5 Learner's own response, but could include:
   - Every three minutes someone dies from cardiovascular disease in the UK.
   - 41,000 people under 75 die from cardiovascular disease each year.
   - One in five adults smokes.
   - Over a third of adults are classed as overweight.
   - Two out of five adults do not achieve recommended levels of physical activity.
   - Only a quarter of adults consume the recommended five portions of fruit or vegetables a day.
   - In the last 30 years the percentage of 30-year-olds doing under 30 minutes of exercise a day has increased by 35 per cent – from 20 per cent in 1986 to 55 percent in 2016.
   - In the last 30 years the percentage of 30-year-olds doing between 30 minutes and 1 hour of exercise a day has decreased by 32 per cent – from 72 per cent in 1986 to 40 percent in 2016.

The pitch (pages 106–107)

1 Learner's own response.
2 Answer will depend on commission chosen:
   - Informational video – five minutes maximum.
   - Interactive website – at least four pages.
   - Radio advertisement – 90 seconds.
   - Poster campaign – four different posters.
   - Smartphone puzzle game – at least three levels.
3 - To raise awareness of risk factors for cardiovascular disease.
   - To encourage healthy lifestyle choices.
   - To coincide with a 'New You' campaign.
4 Mid-December – to coincide with a 'New You' campaign in the new year.
5 Learner's own response, but should always link the features to the key point of the commission.
6 Learner's own response, but should refer and compare to other products in the market.
7 Learner's own response.

Planning the proposal (pages 107–109)

1 Learner's own response.
2 Learner's own response.
3 Learner's own response.
4 Learner's own response, but should address the target audience's journey from beginning to end.
5 Learner's own response, but should be a 'call to action' that is relevant to the aim of the commission chosen.
6 Learner's own response, and will depend on the medium chosen to work in.
7 Learner's own response, but should consider, if relevant to content, legal implications of any content about specific tobacco or alcohol companies, and ensure ethical standards around the treatment of people at high risk of cardiovascular disease.
8 Mid-December.
9 Learner's own response, and will depend on the medium chosen to work in. The response should include opportunities for the client to feed back, and for feedback to be acted upon.
10 Learner's own response, and will depend on the medium chosen to work in.

2. Responding to a commission

Rationale (pages 110–112)

Explain what key information you noted from the brief and how this helped to guide your initial investigations.
Learner's own response, but could include references to the following:
- Every three minutes someone dies from cardiovascular disease in the UK.
- 41,000 people under 75 die from cardiovascular disease each year.
- One in five adults smokes.
- Over a third of adults are classed as overweight.
- Two out of five adults do not achieve recommended levels of physical activity.
- Only a quarter of adults consume the recommended five portions of fruit or vegetables a day.
- In the last 30 years the percentage of 30-year-olds doing under 30 minutes of exercise a day has increased by 35 per cent – from 20 per cent in 1986 to 55 percent in 2016.
- In the last 30 years the percentage of 30-year-olds doing between 30 minutes and 1 hour of exercise a day has decreased by 32 per cent – from 72 per cent in 1986 to 40 percent in 2016.

Explain in detail how you have used the content of the brief in developing your work, referring to specific examples from the information you were provided.
Learner's own response, but should include specific references to the points raised in the previous question.

Explain in detail how the ideas you have proposed meet the specific nature of the commission you were given.
Learner's own response, and will depend on the commission they have chosen.

How would you justify, with specific examples from your own research and investigation, why you have made your suggestions?
Learner's own response, and will depend on the commission they have chosen, but must include reasons why suggestions have been made.

What specific examples of similar existing work have inspired or informed your work and what did you learn from them?
Learner's own response.

Pitch (pages 113–114)

Begin by stating which commission you chose to take forward and why you chose this one. Use positive and persuasive words. This should be one short sentence.
Learner's own response.

Explain why you find this an engaging or interesting commission to respond to. Remember to maintain your persuasive tone by being positive and enthusiastic.
Learner's own response.

Give a two-sentence overview of the nature of the product you have generated ideas for.
Learner's own response.

Explain how this idea meets the brief, and why. Give examples of how it would appeal to the target audience, communicate the intended message and promote the client's cause.
Learner's own response, but could include references to:
- age group of target audience
- ways in which ideas match the demands of the client
- comparison to other products or services consumed by this target audience.

Explain in detail a particular element or detail of the product that you feel makes your idea unique and stronger than competing products.
Learner's own response, but should refer/compare specifically to at least one other product.

Proposal (pages 115–122)
Content overview
Learner's own response.

Technical considerations
Learner's own response.

Contributors, assets, locations and equipment
Learner's own response.

Legal and ethical considerations
Learner's own response.

Scheduling and planning considerations
Learner's own response.

Treatment (pages 123–125)
Learner's own response, and will depend on the commission they have chosen.

Revision task 2

1. Formulating ideas in response to a commission (pages 126–129)

Learner's own response, but should pull out/refer to key points facts and figures in the brief, such as:

- Child casualties a significant issue.
- 7808 under 16s injured or killed on UK roads in 2011.
- Client's aim is to highlight importance to children and parents of wearing luminescent and reflective clothes and accessories in the dark.
- Target audience is young people aged 11–12.
- Target audience particularly at risk due to walking to and from school for first time unsupervised, therefore could be less careful about their road use.
- Client wants to educate and instruct without preaching or judging.
- Client's funding comes from a mix of government, charitable and business sources.
- Road accidents account of over half of all accidental deaths among 5–14-year-olds.
- 11- and 12-year-olds most at risk.
- 11-year-old twice as likely to be seriously injured as a 10-year-old.
- 40 per cent of secondary school pupils walk to school unsupervised.
- Six out of ten 11–12-year-olds say they have had a 'near miss' on the roads.
- 31 per cent of 11–12-year-olds do not wear anything reflective.
- 35 per cent of 11–12-year-olds do not know why they need to wear reflective clothing.
- 38 per cent of 11–12-year-olds know why they need to wear reflective clothing but don't do so.

Ideas and plans, depending on commission chosen, should take into account the length/duration/extent/deadline the client has specified:

- Promotional video – six minutes maximum.
- Mobile phone-accessible website – at least five pages.
- Podcast – six minutes maximum.
- Leaflet – six-page colour leaflet.
- Web-based platform game – at least two levels.
- Deadline for all media is early September.

2. Responding to a commission

Rationale (pages 130–131)

Learner's own response, depending on the commission chosen, but should include specific references to the client's aims, target audience and key points from their notes taken from the brief.

Pitch (pages 132–133)

Learner's own response, but should include:

- an outline of the nature of the product
- how this will meet the needs of the client
- how this will target an audience.

Proposal (pages 134–138)

Content overview
Learner's own response.

Technical considerations
Learner's own response.

Contributors, assets, locations and equipment
Learner's own response.

Legal and ethical considerations
Learner's own response.

Scheduling and planning considerations
Learner's own response.

Treatment (pages 139–148)

Learner's own response and will depend on the commission they have chosen.

Notes

Notes

Notes

Notes